ENTERTAIN

Enjoy a
a var

FOOD + DRINK

Over recent years Leeds has transformed a tepid slop into a gastronomic hotpot.

MUSIC + NIGHTLIFE

Gigs and nights of all genres by bands and DJs of all sizes in venues of all atmospheres

SHOPPING + LIFESTYLE

An eclectic array of fine independent stores add an expertise, quality and care to Leeds.

LIKE OUR STYLE?

TAKE THE LONG ROAD AND WALK IT

John Barran takes you on a walk around our town to help you discover your independent treasures.

Leeds is a big hard city with a small soft centre. Against other sprawling metropolises, it is manageable to navigate through the comparatively compact high streets filled with bright lights and shiny shops. In amongst these are a myriad of independent treasures to stumble upon, sometimes apparent, often to be sought. As is the independent nature, it is ever evolving, expanding and exploring the low roads to discover the rainbow's end. We hope to guide you through the less trodden paths to your pot of gold.

Starting in the centre, where the cost is high and the competition is fierce, there remains strong independent businesses continuing to excel. Shopping centre Trinity has welcomed independents alongside big brands, in particular revolving street food operators in Trinity Kitchen and spicy permanents Rola Wala, Pintura and Cielo Blanco.

Within meters of main shopping strip Briggate there are clusters of independent offerings, notably in stunning Arcades – Thornton's, Queen's and Victoria Quarter – in which you'll find specialist stores selling expertise in books, jewellery, fashion, hair, art, drinks and a whole lot more.

At the bottom of the street is the unsurprisingly named Lower Briggate and its row of eateries and drinkeries, including the aptly named Hedonist Project. The fun continues onto the lively Call Lane where over a dozen impressive independent bars keep it Leeds' most popular nightspot.

The mother of Leeds independents and the heart of the city, geographically and metaphorically, is Kirkgate Market. Inside and out, this iconic site is full of life breathed by stallholders showcasing tradition, soul and some damn fine goods too. Being renovated, the market continues to thrive.

Nearby Kirkgate and Harper Street have been regenerated more organically thanks to the arrival of newcomers such as Fred Aldous, Wapentake and Art Hostel joining residents Cord Barbers, Crowd of Favours and OddfellowsTattoo Collective.

All of which is without mentioning the city's original alternative hotspot, the Corn Exchange. This spectacular building was once the counter-culture hang-out and has returned to similar ways, now filled with intriguing shops and quality lunch stops.

INDEPENDENT TREASURE SEEKER

ENTERTAINMENT + CULTURE

MUSIC + NIGHTLIFE

FOOD + DRINK

SHOPPING + LIFESTYLE

MOORTOWN JUNK-TION
THE REAL JUNK FOOD PROJECT

After veering off on The Headrow for the all-encompassing Headrow House and Crash Records, enjoy Leeds' newly-christened Northern Quarter. Joining North Bar on New Briggate is a recent surge of awesome independent bars on Merrion Street, Cross Belgrave Street, Vicar Lane and North Street. The latter's run of gems, taking in The Reliance and Greedy Pig, have turned a dying part of the city into one of its most essential.

Still other areas are rejuvenated and dazzle because of groupings of independent openings; Laynes Espresso and Friends of Ham are amongst those turning New Station Street into the country's coolest train surround, and Bundobust has sparked an influx of greatness on Mill Hill.

Further south, the idyllic Granary Wharf has been taken over by excellent neighbouring independents, and on the east a gathering also sits on Great George Street. Others stand proudly alone, such as The Decanter on Park Row, Jumbo Records in St John's Centre and La Bottega Milanese in The Light.

And that's just the city centre. The suburbs sprawl to Hyde Park, Brudenell Social Club and its Picture House, to Headingley and its student delights, and to all sides of this glorious city, made better by its inspiring people providing their inspired treasures to all who seek.

WELCOME TO OUR WONDROUS CITY

By Mick McCann, photography by Mike Medlock

I love Leeds me. It's my city; I own it. So if anyone wants to buy Leeds Town Hall, let me know, I'll do you a deal.

My name's Mick, I'm head honcho at independent punk publisher Armley Press and author of the book How Leeds Changed The World, a playful, chatty, factual encyclopaedia of Leeds. It went down quite well - Leeds Waterstones' top selling Christmas book two years in a row - and was chosen by Leeds City Council to be given as a gift from the city to the 800 visiting VIPs for the Tour De France Grand Depart 2014.

Independent Leeds have asked me to do a little intro as I store daft facts about the city I love. Stuff like, the very first statement of the modern green movement was made over 200 years ago by Founding Father' of the United States Ben Franklin as he chatted over a coffee in Leeds, with Joseph Priestley, about Joseph's discovery of photosynthesis.

Mad that innit? But how's about the influence of philosopher David Hartley (who grew up in Armley) on the theory of evolution before Charles Darwin was even born? Take that, Shrewsbury.

I've a capitalism-crushing passion for independent culture and businesses so I'm more than happy to be writing this. It must be something in the River Aire, as it were independent traders and manufacturers in Leeds at the roots of the UK's top three high street brands.

Independent spirits like Matthew Murray and John Blenkinsop built and ran the world's first functioning and commercially viable steam locomotive in Leeds. So you can ignore BBC myth making, George Stephenson directly modelled his first steam locomotive on their work.

Ideas born in Leeds have fundamentally changed the world.

Take John Marshall, a local lad who made his fortune in the city, and was responsible for the building of the world's first iron framed building - the 'grandfather of skyscrapers'. So when you see the New York skyline, know it's rooted in Leeds.

The culture in this city is unrivalled by any other, and our international communities have been at the forefront of it for longer than most of you have been alive. In fact, the annual West Indian Carnival in Chapeltown is Europe's longest running - predating the Notting Hill Carnival by a couple of years.

Leeds also has a rich music scene, and I'm not talking about pasty, depressed youths with beards and acoustic instruments. I grew up with guitar based music and I've seen it all before.

The scenes that are genuinely exciting in Leeds lie in DIY venues such basements and warehouses across the city. This has always been the case too; long before Britain's longest running club night, the legendary Back to Basics, settled in on Lower Briggate, the city played host to the world's first ever disco in the upstairs room of the Ancient Shepherds society.

Coming more up to date, the world owes Leeds a debt for Stickle Bricks, Viagra, Jelly Tots, Spirograph and children's playgrounds. Those aren't in HLCTW, they're material for Volume 2.

So, as my old Dad used to say, 'I know Leeds like the back'a mi hand', and if you don't already, I hope you soon will. It's a wondrous city. xx

For more fascinating facts about our city, pick up How Leeds Changed the World at Waterstones, Amazon, and various places around the city.

CITY PHOTO SYNTHESIS

Leeds Through a Lens revisited by Eleanor Cable and Harry Morris from the University of Leeds.

Managing Performance students, Eleanor Cable and Harry Morris from the University of Leeds, revisited the Leeds through a lens people's photography project, reaching out to the wider city with the theme of 'Seeing Leeds through other people's eyes.' Below they tell their story and introduce some examples from the final 32 showcased at The Gallery at Munro House.

We are Harry and Eleanor, students from the University of Leeds, and co-creators of the Leeds Through A Lens exhibition.

Having lived in Leeds for almost four years, we have both fallen in love with the city and are proud to call it our home. However, during our time here, we have always felt that there is a divide between students, and the wide range of other residents living in Leeds. For this reason, we wanted to unite the two, by exploring the diversity of the city, through the medium of photography.

We invited amateur photographers from around the city to share their view of Leeds, by submitting their pictures and a short paragraph of what the city means to them. With over 250 submissions, we narrowed the photographs down, with the winning pieces being displayed at the Gallery at Munro House for three weeks in April this year.

Sponsored by Studio 81, with Leeds Welcome and Independent Leeds as media partners, we were blown away with the response and the wide range of work that was presented. The exhibition's opening night presented a perfect synthesis between students and long-term Leeds residents, and we were extremely proud that we could fuse the two together and host such a memorable celebration.

We hope that this is a relationship and idea that can be taken further as Leeds continues to develop as a thriving university city. We have grown to love Leeds, not just because of the fantastic student life it offers, but because of the people that were here before us who have made it what it is.

Look out for the full exhibition on our sister site Leedswelcome.com

Danny Hewitt, Civil Servant

To me, this picture highlights the innovation, expansion and enterprise within Leeds. The design of the new entrance is visually stunning, but it also combines with the audible effect of the River Aire flowing through Granary Wharf to offer a unique sensory experience for all travellers.

Fan Liu, Student

This photo was taken on 1st November 2015 near Victoria Quarter. Most pedlars have left at that time on Sunday. This lady packed all her stuff after a hard-working day and was waiting for her son's car to take her home. There is a Chinese idiom describing the lady's state of mind at that moment, called Gui Xin Si Jian, which means that someone is eager to dart homeward like the swiftness of an arrow.

Carlos Ortiz, Photographer

This photo was taken in the heart of Leeds. I stopped at the corner of a shop, with the lights shining in different directions, casting multiple shadows. This gentleman did the rest. 1/12/2015

David Cole, Photographer

The visual isolation of each individual in the snow here reminds me of a Lowry painting and his depiction of the collective community spirit. There is something heart-warming when I see the community coming together to enjoy such a simple pleasure.

Hazel Millichamp,
Student Education Officer

Hunslet Mill and Victoria Works Complex is a series of very large disused mill buildings in Goodman Street, Leeds

Thien Phuc Ton, Student

Leeds itself is a beautiful city. As an international student studying in Leeds, I always find myself wandering between streets and beneath the tall and unique buildings that Leeds has to offer. This photo was taken on the Leeds University Campus.

Paul McKendrick, Musician

I have travelled extensively but feel Leeds can hold its own against the major cities; diversity and architecture are so strong in this great city. This photo was taken of a fairground ride in Millennium Square.

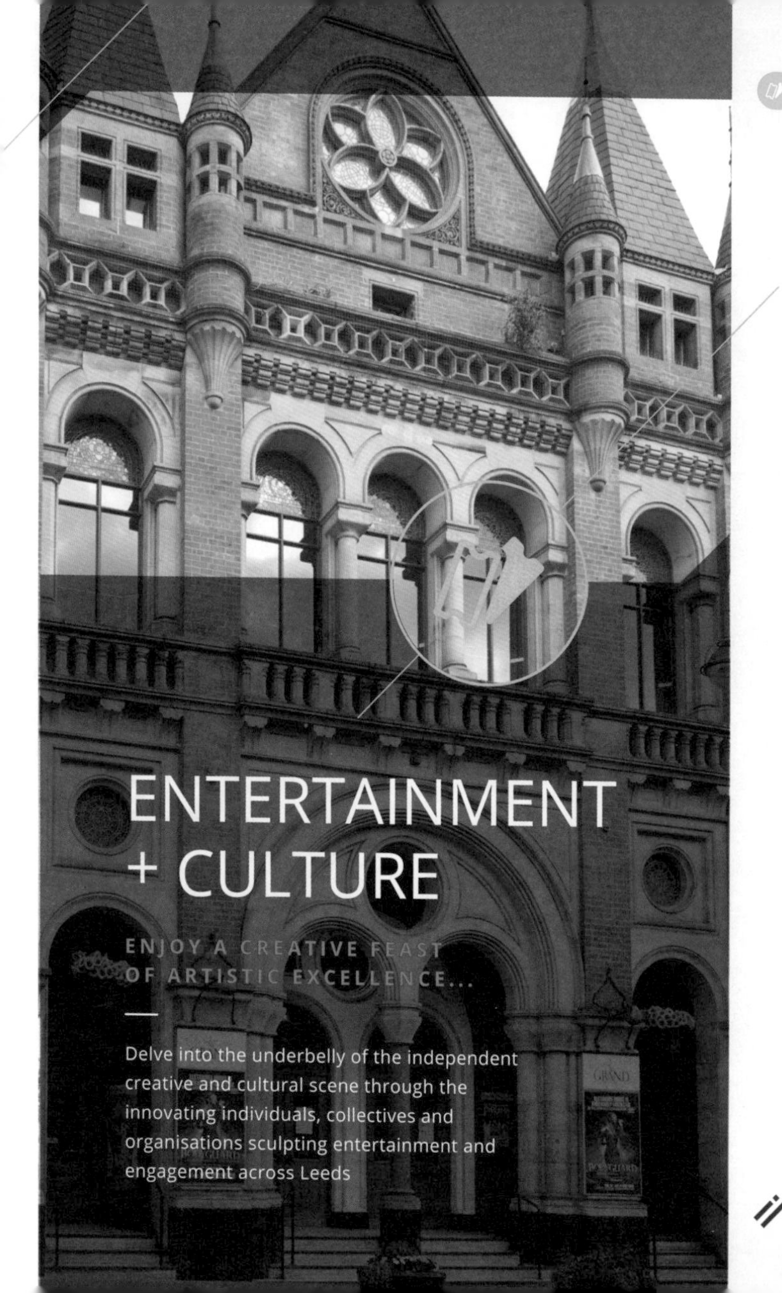

ENTERTAINMENT + CULTURE

ENJOY A CREATIVE FEAST OF ARTISTIC EXCELLENCE...

Delve into the underbelly of the independent creative and cultural scene through the innovating individuals, collectives and organisations sculpting entertainment and engagement across Leeds

STRONGER TOGETHER

the power of collaboration by Matt Burman, Artistic Director, Yorkshire Festival; Photography by Tim Smith'

Returning to Leeds after some years away I have been struck by something that we might all instinctively know but not often shout about or recognise day to day; the generosity and welcome that real people, people in shops, bars, cafes and venues and makers and creators across Leeds show to those new to the city. That we don't articulate that (or maybe you do) is because its something threaded at the deepest level through all that we do.

Embarking on developing a new international festival meant I wanted to meet and talk with people – artists, companies, venues, collectives, small and large – to create and curate something new that didn't ignore all the excellent work that is already happening, that it couldn't be plonked on top of an already busy calendar or exist in some kind of creative vacuum. The first question I asked and will continue to ask - "what is it that we could do together that we can't do separately?", how are we stronger together, how can the sum become greater than its parts? The answers to that question helped shape the programme for Yorkshire Festival 2016 and has also made a fantastic platform – a palette of opportunity – for future years as well.

It perhaps doesn't need saying that festivals are all about collaboration. Without the collaboration of artists, programmers, producers, designers, technicians, makers, volunteers, communities, audiences, venues, funders and sponsors, festivals just don't work, or maybe they do but I'd hazard that at least one of that list wouldn't be happy. And Leeds has more festivals per head of audience than any other city in the country (an authentic made up fact). The spirit and ethos of collaboration is tangible from Transform to Leeds Digital Festival

to Live at Leeds to Leeds Indie Food and that's just one month's worth. Large organisations working with smaller set-ups, commercial companies working with subsidised artists, voluntary groups working with big name writers. That's one superfertile, radical, progressive ecosystem right there. An ecosystem that will continue to enhance, enrich and grow the culture of this city, and with that energy no doubt the rest of the county's too.

Of course its not all about festivals. There's innovative collaboration between sport and art (thinking about Leeds Rhinos dance project developed in collaboration with Cape UK or East Street Arts work in Lille and Ghent, also representing a nice bit of international partnership). And we vitally need the partnership and collaboration of business too; sometimes with logistics (using empty shops for community projects for instance) but also for their vision and philanthropy (supporting projects financially to realise our ambitions). All of those people producing programmes year round, year on year are working together with communities and artists all the time; whether its Opera North and West Yorkshire Playhouse, or the work that Leeds' three universities co-create

I was stumped momentarily in an interview situation when I was asked to talk about collaboration in my work, because pretty much every hour of every working day (and sometimes into the hours of social working outside the nine to five) holds an example of collaboration. And its not just about making and creating work but also about those who view or experience the finished article or performance. A director friend talks about the audience as the last performer, the final collaborative piece of the jigsaw, in making their work. Without the collaboration of the audience, the customer and client, none of us would be doing what we're doing and changing the world one experience, one encounter at a time.

INDEPENDENT THEATRE & PERFORMANCE IN LEEDS

Amy Letman, producer & curator, reflects upon the thriving independent performance culture in the city

You might not know already, that the theatre and performance scene in Leeds is growing and increasingly rivals many major European cities.

Within the context of the performing arts, independents are usually considered those who are not regularly funded, or those who sit outside of more mainstream or building based theatres and structures. Inevitably, not having regular funding comes with pressures and difficulties. So many artists and companies in Leeds seem almost defiant in the face of such pressures, resourceful in their ability to make things happen. There is a fiercely independent spirit to much of the work created in Leeds, artists who resist definition, experimenting with all kinds of ways to create work – be it theatre, live art, dance, the visual, digital or interactive – so much of the performance created in the city seems to operate in the spaces between each of these things. Performance is being made in all kinds of contexts and spaces, and collaboration is rife in the city, not only between different artists and companies, but with local communities and audiences.

In recent years, funding available through Leeds Inspired (part of Leeds City Council) has enabled independent artists and organisations to take more of a lead and make work that feels increasingly responsive to its environment. Projects such as 'Dark and Lovely' by Selina Thompson (a touring show created following a series of residencies in salons and beauty shops in Chapeltown, where Selina collected stories and opinions to explore afro hair, its politics and connotations), 'Roseville Road' by site-specific company A Quiet Word (a walking performance celebrating the life and history of Roseville Road) and 'The Weather Café' by theatre designer David Shearing (an immersive café space emerging on the Headrow, which incorporated the voices of over 100 people living and connected to Leeds), are just a few inspiring

examples of these community engaged projects, and of projects happening outside of traditional spaces and led by independents.

Beyond these extraordinary, one off projects which continue to emerge, there are a number of ways to see and be part of the vivid independent performance scene in Leeds, through festivals, DIY venues and other platforms. The organisation I run, Transform (which began life at West Yorkshire Playhouse in 2011, before setting up as an indie company in 2014) produces regular April festivals of adventurous theatre and performance, by artists from Leeds and around the world, and will present its next edition in 2017. In the meantime, the fantastic Compass Festival of Live Art will return to Leeds in November 2016, offering an inspiring programme of socially engaged live art in the public realm, performances and events, most of which are free to attend. An array of other micro festivals and platforms will be sure to emerge throughout the year, thanks to the ongoing hard work of various artists and producers across the city.

Beyond the festivals, there are venues in the city supporting and presenting independent artists, be it through West Yorkshire Playhouse's Furnace scratch nights, Yorkshire Dance's regular programmes, and studio spaces like Stage@Leeds. The brilliant theatre company Slung Low's home in Holbeck (The HUB) is a set of five railway arches incorporating a makeshift performance space where visiting artists can develop new projects or present performances on a Pay What You Decide basis.

Over on Regent Street, the remarkable Live Art Bistro is an artist led venue offering professional development opportunities to practitioners and hosting an incredible programme of live art, experimental performance, parties and events. Its growth as a home for artists in the last year has been astonishing, and if you're looking for a taster of the independent performance scene in Leeds, this is one place you're definitely set to get it. Expect the unexpected, and to get home late.

Beyond all that is happening on our doorsteps, performance makers and companies who call Leeds their home are being commissioned by and appearing in festivals and venues nationally and internationally, as what is home

grown in Leeds extends beyond Yorkshire, out into the world.

It's impossible to pinpoint this expansive, ever evolving and vibrant community in one section of this directory. The following contains a few reflections from just a handful of independent artists, companies and producers who call Leeds their home. Now it's your turn to go and meet the rest, seek out the incredible projects, festivals and events which reflect Leeds' awesome independent performance culture, and become part of it.

A handful of leeds based artists and producers to reflect upon what leeds' independent performance scene means to them....

Live Art Bistro work exceptionally hard to provide an alternative and inclusive space for people who are interested in performance to experiment and take risks. All we ever seem to encounter is encouragement which makes us proud of our city and our place within it. Having travelled to much of the UK, I honestly feel that we have one of the best independent performance scenes in the country!
Adam Young, Live Art Bistro

Red Ladder came to Leeds from London in the early 70's and yet when I took over ten years ago the company was not part of the fabric of the city - Leeds was just our base. Now the city has a vibrant artistic community with so many exciting artistic conversations in many different alternative and 'underground' venues and melting pots. Most important of all, the Leeds theatre community works together in solidarity and mutual respect. I have never known this non-competitive respectful support anywhere in the UK. It explains why so much good work is born in Leeds.
Rod Dixon, Red Ladder

I am constantly inspired by all of the other artists working in the city. There is a very supportive network comprising not only of artists but of independent producers, designers and venues that all work together, cheering each other on and get projects off the ground. I am so proud of to be a part of the creative scene here and work with the people that I do.
Lydia Cottrell, Artist & Performer

Leeds is home. It has been a place that's given me time and space to grow as writer. The networks that I have, have grown over the years. They've seen me move from a young poet to a published playwright. They have consistently supported that growth at home and beyond Yorkshire. I travel and make new networks, but I know that in Leeds there is a community that I can always come back to.
Zodwa Nyoni, Playwright

Leeds independent performance scene is typified by a sense of anarchic and playful resourcefulness. There is a spirit

of disruptiveness tinged with a little bit of old fashioned Yorkshire belligerence among the city's artists that characterises both the work and the way that it is made. It would be impossible to lump the artists here together as any kind of cohesive movement; then again that's part of the fun of this chaotic, fiercely independent, overwhelmingly supportive, and downright rowdy arts scene.
Uncanny Theatre

Making the move to Leeds from Manchester was the best thing I ever did. After graduating from Northern School of Contemporary Dance, as an independent dancer and maker, I've found the support, friendships and opportunities to enable me to make the things I want to make here. I work all over the country and increasingly internationally, but I always love coming home and being part of the Leeds independent family.
Hannah Buckley

It feels like a really exciting time to be part of the scene in Leeds, there's a really great energy and a lot of collaboration across disciplines. Leeds' brand of independence is being exported out of the city. We travel all over the world to show our work, but Leeds is an environment that allows us to make and develop our work, it's spirit is in everything we create.
Invisible Flock

The work in Leeds often reflects an ethic about the concerns and experience of the wider community, as well as a way of relating to audiences that invites them to take an artistic risk with us. Challenges include obvious things: a precarious business model, related difficulties of planning and development, and the sheer hard work of survival. It's a DIY culture, which doesn't in any way imply a lack of quality or ambition in the work
Alison Andrews, A Quiet Word

I decided to base myself in Leeds because the support from the arts community is not comparable to other cities. I find that every discipline has it's own strong community and identity that implants on the city. As an emerging producer, if I need help and advice there's someone to ask and I don't feel embarrassed or scared to fail as I know I have a strong community behind me.
Melanie Purdie, Producer

Photography courtesy of: Transform, Live Art Bistro, Selina Thompson

LEEDS FILM CITY

By Chris Fell Director, Leeds International Film Festival

Did you know that the world's first moving images were not filmed in Paris or New York, but here in Leeds in 1888 by French inventor Louis Le Prince? The names of the Lumiere Brothers and Thomas Edison are more associated with cinema's early years as Le Prince disappeared in 1891 in mysterious circumstances, but he took the first step with his few frames of traffic on Leeds Bridge and a garden scene in Roundhay. Today, Leeds is alive with the pioneering creative spirit of Le Prince and the city is one of the most exciting centres for film culture in Europe. Here is a selection of some of the highlights of the Leeds film experience: for a full picture of what's happening check out our new website leedsfilmcity.com, launching late in 2016.

You can see films in Leeds in an incredible variety of venues and settings across the city. The much loved Hyde Park Picture House and The Cottage Road Cinema in Headingley, both renowned around the UK, were built just two decades after Le Prince disappeared and they are still showing films after recently celebrating their centenary anniversaries. The first luxury Everyman cinema to be built outside of London opened in Leeds in 2013 and the city has four multiplexes with 52 screens, including the recently transformed Showcase. Regular screenings also take place in dozens of other venues, from the local filmmaking supported by Oblong Cinema at Woodhouse Community Centre to the award-winning international programming of Minicine at Armley Mills, where you can also learn more about Louis le Prince. Films don't have to be shown indoors and in Leeds you can see outdoor screenings at landmark sites such as Millennium Square

and historic buildings like Kirkstall Abbey, where Sneaky Experience present their popular live cinema shows for families.

One of the largest events of its kind in the UK, Leeds international Film Festival (LIFF) celebrates its 30th anniversary this year with a vast selection of over 300 films screening at 16 venues over two weeks in November. Started by volunteers at the Hyde Park Picture House in 1987, LIFF is one of the city's annual cultural highlights and is recognised as a qualifying event for both the Oscars and the BAFTAs. Leeds Young Film Festival (LYFF) is the city's largest Easter event for families, featuring fantastic interactive experiences at Leeds Town Hall and the Carriageworks, where young people can learn how to make their own films or meet their favourite film and TV characters.

Young people are at the heart of a vibrant independent filmmaking industry in Leeds. Many young and successful directors and producers who are at work in the city started out on one of LYFF's training programmes or attended the Northern Film School at Leeds Beckett University, including the filmmakers behind the Oscar-nominated short film Shok. Many rising independent production companies are also at work in the city, including Blackbox, Shot by Sodium and Studio 12.

ANGEL OF YOUTHS

CHARITY | CITY CENTRE

Symons House, Belgrave Street
LS2 8JP

MONDAY, TUESDAY & FRIDAY | 09:00 - 15:00
WEDNESDAY | CLOSED
FRIDAY | 09:00 - 12:30

0113 223 4292
www.angelofyouths.com

DID YOU KNOW?
Angel of Youths provide support to organisations, families & young adults, while linking communities to learning, employment & enterprise.

NO DREAM IS TOO BIG OR TOO SMALL

Angel of Youths was designed to explore the relationship between community development and youth social action.

This innovative Youth Social Enterprise main focus is on building social action projects that will make an impact on youth culture in Leeds; included are opportunities for youths to mentor and coach other young adults through events and an exciting panoply of workshops.

Encouraging youths to play responsible and significant roles in their local communities to meet societal expectations, in the bid to restore lost or shaken confidence in our youths.

THE ART HOSTEL

ARTIST HOSTEL | CITY CENTRE

83 Kirkgate
LS2 7DJ

MONDAY - SUNDAY | 24 hours 7 days a week

0113 345 3363
arthostel.org.uk

WHY NOT TRY?

Any of our artist designed rooms, they all have their own unique charm

UK'S FIRST SOCIAL ENTERPRISE ART HOSTEL

East Street Arts brings you the first social enterprise Art Hostel in the UK, providing distinctive accommodation in a playful, creative space. Aiming to change the way people stay, encouraging visitors to contribute to the city of Leeds while they are here, Art Hostel provides a physical infrastructure to make, create, debate, sleep and explore.

Each bedroom is uniquely designed, contemporary and comfortable. The foyer event space hosts artists and visitors, while in the basement a dynamic, rolling programme of events and happenings awaits; the basement can also be hired out.

Staying starts from as little as £22.50 per person per night, with a range of private rooms, through to shared dormitories. Created by artists for everyone to enjoy.

THE HOLBECK UNDERGROUND BALLROOM

PERFORMANCE VENUE | HOLBECK

67-71 Bath Road
LS11 9UA

See website for upcoming performances, workshops and events

www.slunglow.org

DID YOU KNOW?

The HUB is also a rehearsal and workshop space, which we make available to those making performances in the region who have need of it.

HOLBECK'S VERY OWN 'PAY WHAT YOU DECIDE' THEATRE

Slung Low is an award-winning theatre company specialising in making unlikely, ambitious and original adventures for audiences in unusual places. Slung Low runs a makeshift community theatre space The Holbeck Underground Ballroom (The HUB) based in five railway arches in Holbeck, south Leeds.

The HUB offers a regular performance programme, embracing high quality work which might otherwise not be seen in the city. All shows at the HUB are 'Pay What You Decide' - you give the amount of money you think is right after you see the show and 100% of the box office goes directly to the visiting artists.

We look forward to welcoming you.

HYDE PARK BOOK CLUB

ARTS VENUE | HYDE PARK

27 - 29 Headingley Lane
LS6 1BL

MONDAY - FRIDAY | 10:00 - 15:00 & 17:00 - 23:00
SATURDAY - SUNDAY | 10:00 - 23:00

0113 345 5820
www.hydeparkbookclub.co.uk

WHY NOT TRY?

Our Book Club Burger and Hyde Park Hot Dog made from next level veggie meats from the Vegetarian Butcher

COFFEE//ARTS//SPACE//FOOD//WINE//BEER//DJS//PERFORMANCE

Hyde Park Book Club is an arts space serving coffee, beers, wines and food on Leeds' Hyde Park Corner. Through the day, a chilled out space to hang out, eat, meet, read or write. At night, an array of the most interesting creative groups from the city pop by to speak, perform, exhibit and play. A midweek techno supper club, a spoken word event, a book launch, a live band or djs. HPBC are the UK's only Vegetarian Butcher outlet, with vegetarian burgers, hot dogs and vegan chicken wraps brought over from Holland. Coffee is supplied by Leeds roasters Maude and they are carefully curated from the likes of the city's own Northern Monk. This is alongside a regularly changed group of wines, and a bunch of tasty snacks.

HYDE PARK PICTURE HOUSE

CINEMA | HYDE PARK

73 Brudenell Road
LS6 1JD

MON - TUES & THURS - FRI | 18:00 - 23:00
WEDNESDAY | 11:00 - 23:00
SATURDAY & SUNDAY | 12:00 - 23:00

0113 275 2045
www.hydeparkpicturehouse.co.uk

DID YOU KNOW?

They're a not-for-profit charity. This means they don't charge silly prices. Tickets start from only £4.60

THE COSIEST CINEMA IN LEEDS

Established in 1914, the Hyde Park Picture House is one of the UK's oldest cinemas.

They screen the very best independent, art-house & repertory films from around the world, whether it's live musical accompaniments to silent classics or the latest creation from Wes Anderson.

Their Grade II listed building, complete with gas lighting, balcony & plush red curtains, is like a time-capsule. And thanks to comfy seats, the latest projection technology & tasty craft beers available from the foyer, there's no better place to see films in Leeds.

INKWELL ARTS

CHARITY & CAFÉ | CHAPEL ALLERTON

31 Potternewton Lane
LS7 3LW

MONDAY - FRIDAY | 09:00 - 17:00
SATURDAY | 10:00 - 16:00
SUNDAY | Details online for events

0113 307 0108
www.inkwellarts.org.uk

DID YOU KNOW?

Their vegetarian cafe is open from 10am till 4pm. Full details of courses, events and workshops available on their website.

ENRICHING LIVES THROUGH CREATIVITY

Creativity is the key to enriching lives and building stronger communities. Inkwell Arts Centre provides a community hub that feeds your imagination and unlocks artistic potential.

Their family-friendly vegetarian cafe and garden hosts a range of creative classes, workshops, events, music nights and entertainment.

Inkwell is home to professional artists working in digital and traditional media. We hold regular exhibitions showcasing our work and are commissioned to produce animations, film and graphic design.

We support positive mental health encouraging individuals and communities to flourish. Inkwell is a place to be.

LEFT BANK LEEDS

VENUE SPACE | HYDE PARK

Cardigan Road (opposite Milfords)
LS6 1LJ

Opening hours depend on the programme.
Please check the website for details.

07541 765 286
www.leftbankleeds.org.uk

DID YOU KNOW?

Left Bank Leeds is the only licensed bar on Cardigan Road!

A MULTIDISCIPLINARY ARTS VENUE SET IN AN AMAZING SPACE

Left Bank Leeds is an amazing space that inspires and empowers audiences through its eclectic programme of events that promote creativity, connection and wellbeing. Set in a stunning Grade II* Listed former church building with a licensed bar makes an impressive backdrop for their annual LS6 Beer Festival, art exhibitions, live music, cinema, festivals, markets, fairs, photo shoots, conferences, weddings and private functions. Check their website for upcoming events and whilst you're there sign up for their monthly e-newsletter. If you're interested in hiring the space please get in touch to discuss turning your idea into reality; Contact inspiredevents@leftbankleeds.org.uk

LIVE ART BISTRO

ARTIST VENUE | CITY CENTRE

Live Art Bistro

Regent Street
LS2 7QA

MONDAY - SUNDAY | IRREGULAR

www.liveartleeds.com 

WHY NOT TRY?

Our regular scratch night NEWK. Visit our webiste for details.

IRREVERENT AND TRANSGRESSIVE PERFORMANCE SPACE

Live Art Bistro is an artist led venue and curatorial team based in Leeds. Our common goal is to support the growth of Live Art practices in the region by providing space and opportunities to local artists, whilst also encouraging artists from further afield to present work in the city.

Setup in 2012, LAB quickly gained international presence as an independent venue offering professional development opportunities to practitioners seeking to take risks and meet new (and often 'uninitiated') audiences. LAB continues to expand its reach and geographic presence, with 2015 seeing various international collaborations being made.

ODI LEEDS

CREATIVE SPACE | CITY CENTRE

3rd Floor, Munro House, Duke Street
LS9 8AG

CO-WORKING | **MONDAY - FRIDAY** | 08:30 - 17:30
FOR HIRE | **MONDAY - SUNDAY**

07570 805107
www.Leeds.theodi.org

DID YOU KNOW?

The ODILeeds is a node of the Open Data Institute, founded by the inventor of the Internet, Tim Berners Lee.

WORKSPACE AND EVENT HIRE FOR ALL

Collaboration and innovation space in Leeds. ODILeeds is a not for profit organisation working to innovate with data in the Leeds City Region. We also have an amazing, large, light-filled loft style workspace in the heart of Leeds city centre, which is perfect for those looking for an independent workspace or venue hire space that is a little bit different from the everyday.

Whether it is pop in co-working, a place to hold a workshop, a meeting, an un-conference, a hackathon or a party, we can meet most requests. With breakout sofa areas, superfast wifi and unlimited tea and coffee, come and join our growing network and benefit from being part of the wider ODILeeds and ODIHQ community. Co-working from £10 per day.

SEVEN

ARTSPACE & CAFE / BAR | CHAPEL ALLERTON

31a Harrogate Road
LS7 3PD

CAFE/BAR OPEN DAILY | FROM 10:30 UNTIL LATE
FOOD SERVED | FROM 11:30 & 17.30 MON - SAT
SATURDAY & SUNDAY BRUNCH | 10:30 - 15:30

0113 262 6777
www.sevenleeds.co.uk

WHY NOT TRY?

As well as our arts programme try our food & cakes, coffees, plus a wide selection of beers, wines & spirits

AN INDEPENDENT ARTS SPACE WITH A DIFFERENCE

Our aim at Seven is to showcase the best of local, national & international talent and to attract innovative work. Providing a hundred-seat venue for theatre, dance, music, words and comedy. Every Monday, Screen Seven shows art house cinema. While the arts programme is jam-packed full of interesting events, many people come to Seven simply to enjoy the café/bar, with a daily changing menu and artwork from local artists on the walls. Now in our eighth year, we continue striving to provide high quality arts to the local community; grab a programme from our website to see what's happening this month at Seven. Thanks to all those that have supported us over the last eight years... and here's to eight more!

THE TETLEY

GALLERY, EVENTS & RESTAURANT | CITY CENTRE

T

Hunslet Road
LS10 1JQ

GALLERY HOURS	
MON - SAT	11:00 - 18:00
SUN	11:00 - 16:00

Open until 8pm on the first Thursday of every month

BAR & KITCHEN HOURS	
MON - FRI	09:00 - 23:00
SAT	10:00 - 23:00
SUN	10:00 - 20:00

0113 320 2323 www.thetetley.org 

WHY NOT TRY?

Exploring the galleries and stopping for a drink in the Bar and Kitchen

A CENTRE FOR CONTEMPORARY ART AND LEARNING

The Tetley is a centre for contemporary art and learning operating from a landmark heritage building - the former Tetley headquarters. The commitment to support early career and emerging artists remains a core value of The Tetley.

Extend your stay in The Bar and Kitchen and sample a delicious Yorkshire inspired menu, and of course there's Tetley's Beer on tap.

All profits from the Bar & Kitchen go directly to supporting our artistic and educational programming at The Tetley, located on the ground floor. Where better to enjoy a pint of Tetley's than where it was born nearly 200 years ago?

TRANSFORM

THEATRE | ACROSS LEEDS

TRANSFORM

West Yorkshire PlayhousePlayhouse Square
LS2 7UP

Visit the website to view upcoming events

www.transformfestival.org

WHY NOT TRY?

visit our website for artist opportunities and special events

REIMAGINING WHAT THEATRE CAN LOOK LIKE

Presenting festivals of performance from Leeds and internationally, whilst concocting projects with bold artists all year round, Transform presents theatre works everywhere from arts venues across Leeds, to city sites and outdoor spaces. Celebrating the independent and adventurous spirit of Leeds, we want to reflect the socially conscious and radical North, whilst connecting to the world. Transform was originally established by West Yorkshire Playhouse in 2011. Setting out to reimagine what theatre can look like and what it can do, the annual Transform festivals take place across the theatre building and outside its doors in a range of sites and spaces.

WHEN DID IT GET SO GOOD?

An Introduction to The Leeds Art Scene by John Slemensek

I started here as a young art student ready to take on whatever this exciting city of Leeds could give me. It sure offered me a whole lot of opportunity. Where was the grassroots arts and culture? Where can I access the most unique parts of the city? I kept digging, and I found that the true foundation of the Leeds Art Scene is in the people!

Together we started to plant our own foundations in the holes that we had dug in our search for treasure. We supported each other, we collaborated, and we gave everything we had to make things happen. Now I am BOKEHGO and I document the happenings all around the city that others are doing to an extraordinary level

Over the next few pages you will see a few projects that I find particularly inspiring. Throughout my time in Leeds I have been unceasingly amazed by what these people are achieving and I am proud to present them to you.

Welcome to Leeds' Art Scene my friends, enjoy your exploration. Truly DIY...

Assembly House / Lady Beck

In 2013 the seeds of something exciting began to emerge as graduates from Leeds College of Art saw the opportunity to stick together and make a mark in the city. Their initial ambition was simple and came to fruition in the form of Assembly House.

Based in Armley, Assembly House now houses 21 studio holders and is known for its diverse and often experimental shows of emerging artists in a space that is fun, challenging and occasionally mischievous.

In 2014 the organisation incorporated as a Community Interest Company and secured regular funding from Leeds City Council. In 2016 Assembly House are to launch Lady Beck, an exciting second space in Mabgate

Making it happen...

Byron Street Studios / Temple of Boom

Byron Street Studios is a collection of small businesses who create by hand. We're D.I.Y to the bone and the struggle produces incredible things. We've done it all on our own terms, in our own time and in our own way.

Now, 5 years in, we're still making it up as we go along... we're just better adjusted to the roller-coaster of running creative enterprises and accept the exciting journey. Being a community gives Byron St Mills its spirit.

Engaging People...

Inkwell Arts / Arts & Minds

Arts & Minds is a network of people who are interested in the link between creativity and good mental health. We work within the NHS to encourage mental health services to use creativity and the arts. Every October, Arts & Minds run Love Arts Festival, an annual celebration of creativity and mental well-being. We want as many people in the city to use the arts to open up conversations about mental health and to spread the word that being creative is good for you.

Live Art Bistro

LAB forms an essential site and service for many young and emerging artists and companies who create performance that wouldn't strictly be classed as

theatre. Much of this type of work happens in unusual spaces and involves acknowledging the audience is present.. We create the space for performers to challenge assumptions, test out ideas and take measured risks in an 'open to all' atmosphere.

Making Space for Artists...

East Street Arts

Patrick Studios is a bespoke venue for artists and provides up to 34 quality studio spaces, resource areas, a double height Project Space and the office and headquarters of East Street Arts

Barkston House is a studio facility and ceramics centre located on Domestic Street Light Industrial Estate in Holbeck, Leeds. East Street Arts currently occupies seven units on the building's third floor, which are home to 40 studio spaces, a ceramics facility, a classroom able to accommodate

20 people and two residency spaces.

Union 105's remit is to support artists based in Chapeltown through its seven studios. The small, off-street Project Space hosts work by commissioned artists and partner events.

The Art Hostel is the first social enterprise Art Hostel in the UK, created by artists for everyone to enjoy.

Making a Difference…

Seagulls Reuse

Seagulls is an environmental social enterprise decorator's merchants, distributing quality reclaimed paint, whilst supporting local communities and the planet.

To put one of Seagulls' achievements into perspective: They have saved enough paint from going to landfill to paint every room in over 15,000 back to back terraced houses. Now that's a lot of happy and beautiful homes.

Innovative thinkers providing unique places…

Champion Up North /
The Old Red Bus Station

Champion Up North is a multi-platform media brand specialising in music, arts, culture and communication.

The Old Red Bus Station is their new home, built almost entirely from reclaimed materials. A multi-purpose venue, bar, canteen and creative offices, the venue plays host to a carefully curated programme of arts and music events.

BasementArtsProject

At the centre of a small terrace house in Beeston is what could be Leeds' smallest art venue; but what BasementArtsProject lacks in physical scale it makes up for in its ambitions. It is an ideologically neutral space in which artists are in complete control of their vision. With a little imagination and fewer rules, the only limitation becomes cost and that is not insurmountable.

Leanne Buchan, Principal Officer
Culture and Sport Leeds City Council

I've always found Leeds a strangely addictive place. It has great monoliths of culture and art that

continue to surprise and delight and push boundaries, but in a thoroughly Leeds way.

What often attracts me most is the Leeds that could easily pass you by if you weren't looking for it. The Leeds teaming with bars, cafes, restaurants and one-off dining experiences, temporary public art and pop-up performances, here one day gone the next.

Increasingly this secret scene is taking on a European flavour. It's not unusual to see Leeds alongside Porto, Berlin, Paris and Barcelona anymore. This is a city with a culture quietly making international waves that aren't always felt on home shores.

Perhaps, with the announcement of the city's intention to bid to become European Capital of Culture 2023, this is set to change. Already a little light is starting to shine on the city's broader culture; there is more to Leeds than meets the eye.

Arguably every city has its unique and hidden talents, but in Leeds it's the people behind these ventures that signal a change in the air. Those people who have the guts to take their passion and turn dream into reality. The people who come together to keep Leeds vibrant, experimental, and always on the look-out for what's next.

The thing that unites these great people and the great cultural organisations of the city is a

blatant disregard for the rule book. A mantra of if it isn't broke, we should break it.

When asked what was on the horizon for the Leeds cultural offer, I hoped it would be more of the same.

Nicola Greenan, External Relations Director East Street Arts

Leeds is my home, the place I grew up and the place I always come back to. Seacroft was my education, my protection, my community, and also my enemy.

In 1990 I was given the chance to get involved in a creative project that changed the direction of my future. This is

why I can wholeheartedly say that arts and culture can truly be transformational. Fast forward many years and I am now a director at East Street Arts.

In 2010 I was running a film booth at the Seacroft Gala asking residents what they thought about the estate and I will never forget the words of one 12 year old boy; "Seacroft is like an Alsatian, if you're on its good side it will protect you, look after you and be loyal, but if you get on its wrong side it could bite your head off". That sentence has stuck with me and resonates in the Leeds arts scene.

It's made me wary of how this can make us behave and can affect the way in which we create projects in this city. We don't always say what we want to say in fear of repercussions. As Chair of Engagement for European Capital of Culture I see one of our major challenges is in 'talking truth to power'. We have a moment in Leeds' history to put arts & culture at the heart of the city and explore the cracks, failings and opportunities to reimagine the way in which people live in this city.

So at risk of being bitten by the Alsatian I am going to tell the truth and challenge some of our elected members to understand the changing culture in our communities, remove hurdles to engagement of seeking permission, and enable people to just get on and do it.

OUR DIGITAL REVOLUTION

By Stuart Clarke, founder Leeds Digital Festival and Director, Media Yorkshire.

Leeds is a city built on innovation, in engineering, in manufacturing, in retail. Over the last twenty years or so, we've been quietly innovating in another field: digital. From offering the UK's first free internet service provider, Freeserve, and the pioneering online news service Ananova, Leeds was at the forefront of the early internet.

Since then the sector has grown rapidly, so much so that over 70,000 people are now employed in the Leeds City Region in the digital sector, working in almost 9,000 firms. Some of those firms are huge employing many hundreds of people: Sky Bet, Callcredit, William Hill and Rockstar Games. Sky moved into Leeds in 2015 and employed over 450 in their first year in the city.

However, the digital scene is not just about the big firms, it also has hundred of smaller firms, creating and innovating in digital health, in data science, in the Internet of Things. A great example is home security firm Cocoon, founded by five locals, and named as one of the top ten key startups in the UK, with its revolutionary 'Subsound' technology. Cocoon was started in Leeds, it's firmly rooted here and being part of the city is key to its values. Other startups making waves include Synap, founded by two Leeds University junior medics, which helps students revise using artificial intelligence methods. We also have dozens of award-winning digital marketing agencies such as Bloom and Marvellous.

You'll find developers, coders, creatives from these independent firms sitting in the many great coffee shops and bars we have in the city, collaborating on the next big idea, creating partnerships, supporting each other with offers of help and work.

And it's this sense of community that is important to the Leeds digital sector: there are around 25 regular meetups, covering all tastes. User experience designers get together for Northern UX; programmers can take their pick

of Code Dojo, Leeds Ruby Thing, Leeds Javascript and others; Hey! Stac brings a mix of business, design and technology.

A few people took the community feel to a different level in April this year. Meeting in a pub, a dozen people in the digital sector, all from smaller firms, decided to stage the Leeds Digital Festival. After just four months of planning, 56 events took place across the city, with over 170 speakers. Of the 56 events, 52 were free, allowing everyone to take part.

The Festival organisers provided a platform, a brand, a reason to celebrate the many different cultures in Leeds, and the city responded: we had events on digital health, on digital art, on digital music due to the collaboration (that word again) with Live at Leeds. We even had the UK debut of Code in the Dark, where developers compete against each other to solve a problem, but they can't see their screens yet the audience can. That was held at The Belgrave Music Hall; along with other venues such Headrow House, Dock 29 and White Cloth Gallery, the Festival came out to the city, rather than expecting the city to come to the Festival.

The next five years will see an extra 10,000 jobs added to the digital sector in the Leeds City Region. Time to build more coffee shops?

FOOD + DRINK

FILL YOUR BELLY AND QUENCH YOUR THIRST...

A handsome selection of independent cafés, bars, restaurants, pop-ups and pubs have revitalised the Leeds culinary experience for all palettes and wallets.

INSIDE OUR FOOD AND DRINK SCENE

by Ben Davy (Belgrave Music Hall / Headrow House)

When I was approached to write a few words on the food and drink scene in Leeds my initial reaction was mild panic.

Where to start? What if I miss someone out? Who really does the best coffee in Leeds? Why would anyone listen to me anyway?

Of course, really none of this matters. So instead I've decided to see this as my opportunity to champion what I consider to be the very best of the Leeds food and drink scene. It's a personal thing - which is surely what enjoying good food and drink is all about.

So, here is a snapshot of my Leeds food and drink highlights. What's really exciting is that I've barely scratched the surface of what's out there - but, for now, it's just you and me spending a day together as we eat and drink our way around this great city...

It's early morning; we need a coffee. Head to Laynes Espresso or La Bottega Milanese. Both of these places have the ability to transport you away from the madness of city centre life.

Breakfast is up next. This is an easy one: the guys at The Greedy Pig do the best breakfasts in Leeds, the house merguez sausage with ducks eggs and harissa is a guaranteed winner. Always quick, always excellent. A fine example of hardworking independents nailing their trade.

What do you fancy for lunch? We could hit Bundobust for some of the best Indian Street Food in the UK. There is some serious skill on display in their kitchen, taking simple ingredients and turning them into something very special.

If we fancy a sit down meal we can head next door to Tharavadu for some authentic, fresh, light Keralan cooking. They're all about the fish, coconut, curry leaves and incredible dosa.

What's your take on Chinese? Red Chilli near Millennium Square is the most authentic Chinese food I've had outside Beijing. Forget westernised Cantonese – this is the real thing. We can be as safe or as brave as we want: the menu has all bases covered.

And if authentic is what we're in the mood for, Thai Aroy Dee is about as authentic as it comes. Big flavours, generous with the chilli, the Som Tam and Pad Gra-Prao will put hairs on your chest.

For a more Westernised nod to Thai, My Thai is cheap and tasty, and we can always expect a warm welcome from Bee and Simon.

Talking of cheap, how about lunch for under a fiver? We could head to Caravanserai next to the Corn Exchange or Café Moor in Kirkgate market: both owned by Kada, who's been peddling his stunning shwarma and falafel in Leeds for over 15 years. We'll even be treated to a free mint tea while we wait.

Talking of falafel, we could visit the boys at Humpit in the Corn Exchange, who do their one-trick-menu of houmous, falafel and freshly baked pitta brilliantly. Simple and perfect.

If charcuterie is up your street, we can always call into Friends of Ham for a mid-afternoon bit on the side. Their thing is (unsurprisingly) meat, cheese and wine.

The Reliance is also a great shout for charcuterie, with all their curing done in house by owner Joss. This place has so much charm and character you'll probably want to move in. Their lunch time and evening menus cover everything from classic fish and chips to thoughtful well executed small plates, with head chef Tom Hunter doing wonderful things with more unusual cuts like goat leg and hogget.

If we're lucky, we might even catch one of the events going on at Leeds Indie Food. Now in its second year, and continuing to go from strength to strength, LIF is 18 days of city-wide collaborations and one-off events from Leeds food and drink businesses at the top of their game. Without a doubt one of the most forward-thinking food festivals in the country.

Dinner is an easy one: let's head slightly out of town to the wonderful Zucco in Meanwood for well cooked, small/sharing plates, served up family style. This is one of those places I don't really want anyone else to know about because I want it all to myself. Alright, they don't really know how to use the internet but who cares? Great food by great people, quietly

getting on with being excellent. My absolute favourite place in Leeds right now.

While we're out that end of town, we can always pop in to House of Koko, a great little café in Chapel Allerton. The kitchen is run by Chef Josh Whitehead and the guy is a genius. His in-house supper clubs have quickly gained a loyal following, and I'm sure it won't be long before he's given somewhere bigger to stretch his culinary wings.

Cash – and space – permitting, The Man Behind the Curtain offers an imaginative tasting menu in a contemporary arthouse space. Booked out months in advance thanks to Michael O'Hare's forward thinking culinary vision, this unique offering has also been gifted the first Michelin star that Leeds has seen since Pool Court.

Need to pick up a few bits to take home? Kirkgate Market – one of Europe's largest remaining indoor markets – is currently undergoing a massive refurbishment. Home to a host of stalls, including a nut shop, a spice lady (the number one dealer of all things spice), butchers, fishmongers (Tarbetts are our go-to guys for the restaurant, sourcing some excellent East Coast day boat catches), cafes, greasy spoons and delis, one step inside the market will give you a true taste of just how multicultural Leeds really is.

Of course, no day out in Leeds is complete without a drink or two. For a cocktail, we can head to Blind Tyger. It's dark, quiet, cosy, largely undiscovered: ticks all my cocktail boxes. Many a night has been lost while perusing their well-considered list.

If wine is more your thing then hit The Reliance, they have a real focus on natural and bio-dynamic wines. Prepare to be educated, their wine knowledge is the greatest in the city.

One of my fondest memories of 2015 was propping up their pop-up bar at the Leeds Beer Festival. That was when the Reli and I fell in love.

One more for the road? Whitelocks and North Bar offer some of the best 'proper' beer in the city – but for a true cheap and cheerful pint, The Angel is the local's favourite.

After a day like that, all that remains is to roll into bed and happily digest the day's offerings.

Is there another city in the country that can rival Leeds' food and drink scene? If there is, I'm yet to discover it...

Food Fiesta illustrations by Louisa Foley
Instagram @louisafoley

ACCOLADES

Highly Commended Newcomer Of The Year
Yorkshire Life Food & Drinks Awards 2015

21 British Street Foods You Must Try Before You Die
Buzzfeed

Game Changer
Olive Magazine

Best Cafe/Bar
YEP Oliver Awards 2015 & 2016

Top 10 UK Indian Restaurants
TimeOut

PRESS

"The dream pairing of craft beer & food."
Shortlist

"Some of best street food in Britain."
Grazia

"A no-two-mouthfuls-the-same delight."
The Guardian

"The food is excellent, the beer on point, & the staff are enthusiastic ambassadors for both."
Olive Magazine

"One of the most anticipated new restaurants to open in Leeds for years."
Waitrose Magazine

"A game changer. Everything it does, it does right."
TimeOut

"I wish that more pubs served spicy okra fries as bar snacks."
New York Times

AAGRAH

RESTAURANT | CITY CENTRE

St Peters Square, Quarry Hill
LS9 8AH

MONDAY - SATURDAY | 17:30 - 24:00
SUNDAY | 16:30 - 22:30

0113 245 5667
www.aagrah.com

WHY NOT TRY?

The Grilled Seafood Menu; it includes some of the finest grilled recipes from the Indian subcontinent, catering for the health conscious.

'THE SULTAN OF SPICE' SATISFACTION, COMFORT AND AFFORDABILITY

Aagrah are about so much more than delivering the quality 'taste of Asia' on a plate...

The Aagrah experience is designed to overwhelm you with a complete sensory journey, encompassing the rich cultural ambience and truly remarkable culinary sensation of authentic Kashmiri cuisine.

Balancing time-honoured dishes with culinary innovation, their hand-picked, award winning team of chefs relentlessly aim to provide healthy and nutritious dishes prepared to nothing less than total satisfaction, in the most comfortable of atmospheres.

ALMOST FAMOUS

BURGER RESTAURANT | CITY CENTRE

23 - 25 Great George Street
LS1 3AL

MONDAY - THURSDAY | 12:00 - 22:00
FRIDAY - SATURDAY | 12:00 - 23:00
SUNDAY | 12:00 - 22:00

0113 397 1337
www.almostfamousburgers.com

WHY NOT TRY?

The 'Shut Up America', a burger with an Oreo ice cream sandwich on top? Yeah really! You'll never know if you don't give it a go.

SERVING DELICIOUSLY NAUGHTY BURGERS & DREAMS DAILY

Almost Famous Burgers has made its way across The Pennines from its home town of Manchester to bring its special brand of burgers, wings and fries to the good people of Leeds.

Everything that made Almost Famous Burgers 'almost famous' is here; over the top burgers like the Triple Nom, decadent and delicious sides like the Bacon Bacon Fries, boozy shakes and a crazy, tricked out interior.

Come and see what all the fuss is about. Come and be Almost Famous.

Burgers & Dreams!

AMBIENTE TAPAS

RESTAURANT | CITY CENTRE

36 – 38 The Calls
LS2 7EW

MONDAY - SUNDAY | 12:00 - 22:00

0113 246 1848
www.ambiente-tapas.co.uk

WHY NOT TRY?

Spend an hour or two sampling our drinks in our beautiful bar or riverside seating area.

EXPERIENCE THE GLORY OF TAPAS

Ambiente's Leeds restaurant is situated on the ground floor of an impressive five story Grade II listed former warehouse on the banks of the River Aire.

With a menu of over thirty hot tapas dishes to choose from, all prepared in full view in the theatre style kitchen, you'll be spoilt for choice and will leave wanting more. So, if you fancy some delicious and freshly cooked tapas (and we should emphasise that its freshly cooked with pans and flames only as there are no microwaves here!) washed down with a glass or two from their expansive, yet inexpensive, wine list then all you need to do is book yourself a table.

In case you need an extra reason to visit... A weekday lunchtime offer of three tapas for a tenner!

THE ARCH CAFE

CAFÉ | CITY CENTRE

Bradbury Building, Mark Lane
LS2 8JA

MONDAY - FRIDAY | 08:30 - 15:30
SATURDAY | 09:00 - 16:30

0113 389 3002
www.thearchcafeleeds.co.uk

DID YOU KNOW?

That you can hire our grade 2 listed venue for private events

A SOCIAL ENTERPRISE CAFÉ IN THE HEART OF LEEDS

We are passionate about baking and fresh local ingredients, and work with some of the region's best local and independent suppliers to serve seasonal and responsibly sourced food and drink. We use a local butcher, our bread is hand baked locally, and all our eggs and mayo are free range.

We serve great coffee, Yorkshire tea, breakfasts and lunches, as well as homemade cakes and afternoon teas. Located in the Grade 2 listed Bradbury Building, the cafe opens into the churchyard of St John the Evangelist.

We aim to be sustainable and socially inclusive, regardless of age, gender or disability. The income from the café supports the great work of Age UK within Leeds and the wider community.

ARCHIE'S BAR & KITCHEN

BAR & RESTAURANT | CITY CENTRE

The Dark Arches, Granary Wharf
LS1 4BR

MONDAY - THURSDAY | 08:00 - 00:00
FRIDAY | 08:00 - 01:00 | **SATURDAY** | 09:00 - 01:00
SUNDAY | 09:00 - 00:00

0113 2431001
www.archiesleeds.co.uk

WHY NOT TRY?

Burger Friday's - All day, every Friday - any burger, fries & a drink for £10.

AN ALL-DAY VENUE WITH A UNIQUE URBAN VIBE, WHERE THE CITY MEETS THE SEA

Set within the riverside location of Granary Wharf, this stylish yet comfortable venue welcomes you to enjoy a variety of food offerings with premium breakfast and all day dinner options. Passionate about delivering high quality and delicious plates of food cooked fresh to order.
The drinks menu features a fantastic range of cocktails, craft beer and real ale, as well as the usual main stream favourites. We serve award winning Grumpy Mule coffee, Brew loose leaf tea and funky juices out of our 1974 VW Campervan, available to drink in or take away. Have you got your dancing shoes at the ready? From 9pm the Archie's dance floor comes to life with our resident DJ every Friday and Saturday night.

ART'S CAFÉ

RESTAURANT | CITY CENTRE

42 Call Lane
LS1 6DT

MONDAY - SUNDAY | 12:00 - 23:00

0113 243 8243
www.artscafebar.com

WHY NOT TRY?

The infamous Sticky Toffee Pudding, which comes with Horlicks butterscotch sauce and Malteser ice cream! The perfect combo!

LEEDS' ORIGINAL CAFE BAR

Having first opened its doors in 1994, Arts Cafe is Leeds' original cafe bar. It is one of the city's favourite eateries, having built a reputation from offering a high quality and interesting menus. This is complemented by regular 6-weekly exhibitions of artwork. Its relaxed atmosphere and friendly staff have made it a popular destination for both lunch and dinner, with its mid-week Early Bird Menu offering three courses for just £15.

The menu is seasonal and regularly updated with an impressive selection of vegetarian dishes.

BANGWOK

RESTAURANT | CITY CENTRE

Sovereign Place
LS1 4SP

MONDAY - FRIDAY | 12:00 - 15:00 & 17:30 - LATE
SATURDAY | 17:30 - LATE

www.bangwok.com 

WHY NOT TRY?

Our beef short rib massaman - it won 'Best Main' at last year's British Street Food awards

NOT YOUR AVERAGE THAI RESTAURANT

After getting a whole lot of love at our pop-up in Trinity Kitchen, we parked up our tuk-tuk and opened our first proper joint in Leeds last year.

If you pop in at lunch, you can enjoy a short menu that's cooked fresh and fast, focusing on ahaan jahn diow – that's a 'one dish meal'. We're talking pad Thai, our legendary sriracha fried rice, salads and curries. They're cheap, filling, healthy and fresh – and guaranteed to have you coming back for more!

In the evening, it's all about the raan gin lao – literally a 'shop to drink liquor'. This is how drinking is done in Thailand. Order an ice-cold Chang beer or a cocktail and a plethora of salty, spicy or fatty kap klaem (bar snacks) and enjoy. Pop gun mai! (See you soon!)

BAR 166 & BISTRO

BAR & BISTRO | HORSFORTH

Bar 166 & Bistro

166 Town Street
LS18 4AQ

MONDAY | CLOSED
TUESDAY - SATURDAY | 12:00 - LATE
SUNDAY | 12:00 - 21:00

0113 322 9910
www.bar166.co.uk

WHY NOT TRY?

Bringing the kids... Kids under 8 eat free on Sundays (1 child per 2 paying adults). Try their award winning Sunday Roasts.

AWARD WINNING SUBURBAN EATERY & BAR IN HORSFORTH

The award-winning, family-run eatery, which opened 10 years ago, is one of the most popular nightspots in the thriving suburb serving locally sourced food, craft ales and cocktails.

The place itself is beautiful, all exposed brickwork and polished wood. And the atmosphere is great too, chilled in the daytime, lively at night. All in all Bar 166 & Bistro is quite a complete venue. It is a stylish yet subtle compromise between city bar and suburban pub.

BILBAO BAR

RESTAURANT / BAR | CITY CENTRE

Arch U, Granary Wharf
LS1 4BR

SUNDAY - THURSDAY | 11:30 - 23:00
FRIDAY & SATURDAY | 11:00 - 00:00

0113 345 4323
www.bilbaobar.co.uk

WHY NOT TRY?

A charcuterie board with finely carved Jamon and Iberico ham

BRINGING A UNIQUE BLEND OF BASQUE CUISINE AND CULTURE TO THE HEART OF LEEDS

Located in one of the railway arches by the riverside in Granary Wharf. Having a warm, laid back and intimate vibe, with a handpicked selection of Spanish and Basque wines, beers and signature cocktails on offer. Feast on a charcuterie board with finely carved Jamon and Iberico ham, and a selection of delicious tapas and pintxos. At any point in time, you could be forgiven for thinking you had stepped into one of the local tapas bars in San Sebastián. The Basque chefs are proud of creating a fusion of dishes that will inspire and delight all taste buds.

One thing is guaranteed, whether you have tried Basque cuisine or not, you'll leave wanting more!

BIRD & BEAST

RESTAURANT | CITY CENTRE

BIRD
& BEAST

Central Arcade, Leeds
LS1 6DX

TUESDAY - SATURDAY | 12:00 - 22:00
SUNDAY | 12:00 - 18:00

0113 245 3348
www.thebirdandbeast.co.uk

WHY NOT TRY?

Our private dining room for up to 20 people or our new Karaoke Beats bar.

THE HOME OF AWESOME CHICKEN

Bird & beast is a Rotisserie restaurant featuring our incredible free range chicken in a range of flavours. We have great ribs, steaks, lamb and pork chops cooked in our wood fired oven. With a great range of other dishes including tandoori, satay, lamb and halloumi kebabs. These are completed with a large selection of salads that change with the seasons and some great sides including our signature "dutch chips" with melted cheese, spring onion and sour cream dip. On Sundays we served a full traditional Sunday lunch of roasted beef, roast lamb or chicken with all the trimmings. Our private dining room holds up to 20 and our set party menu can cater for groups from 10-90 in one go. Top this all up with some great beers, wines, cocktails and milkshakes. Book a private booth in our new Karaoke Beats bar.

BROWN'S GREENS

VEGETARIAN CAFÉ | RAWDON

3B Harrogate Road
LS19 6HW

TUESDAY & WEDNESDAY | 08:30 - 15:30
THURSDAY - SATURDAY | 08:30 - 20:00
SUNDAY | 08:30 - 18:00

0113 239 1489
www.brownsgreens.co.uk

WHY NOT TRY?

Gluten Free? Vegan? We try our best to make sure we always have yummy treats available!

DELICIOUSLY.....HEALTHY, LOCAL, INDEPENDENT VEGGIE CAFE

Located in Rawdon, Brown's Greens is a warm, friendly and independent veggie cafe.

We have a delicious selection of cakes, teas, coffees and fresh veggie delights.......oh and we have wine, Wi-Fi and also a wicked selection of toys and books for the little ones. Bring a friend, bring your family, bring your other half or just bring yourself and relax with the papers, a bite to eat and a bevy.

Come in and see us, and ask about the 'unicorn'.

BUNDOBUST

BAR & STREET FOOD | CITY CENTRE

BUNDOBUST

6 Mill Hill
LS1 5DQ

MONDAY - THURSDAY | 12:00 - 23:00
FRIDAY - SATURDAY | 12:00 - 24:00
SUNDAY | 12:00 - 22:00

0113 243 1248
www.bundobust.com

WHY NOT TRY?

LUNCH EXPRESS Menu. 2 dishes for £7. Available Monday to Friday. 12noon until 4pm.

AWARD WINNING INDIAN STREET FOOD & CRAFT BEER

Bundobust is not a restaurant, it is a bar that sells Indian street food with an extensive selection of the world's best craft beer.

The food, influenced by the vibrant street food scene of India, should be washed down with hoppy India Pale Ales, a classic beer style that was originally brewed in England and shipped to the troops in times of The Raj. Wine and cocktails are also available.

Since opening, Bundobust has fast become the city's go to place for craft beer fans and curry fanatics.

CAFÉ MOOR

CAFÉ | KIRKGATE MARKETS

Stall B, 1904 Market Hall
LS2 7HY

MONDAY - SATURDAY | 10:00 - 17:00
SUNDAY | CLOSED

0113 247 0569
www.cafemoor.co.uk

WHY NOT TRY?

One of Cafe Moor's Award winning North African and Middle Eastern delights!

NORTH AFRICAN AND MIDDLE EASTERN STREET FOOD

To find Café Moor in the heart of Kirkgate Market sniff out the fresh herbs and aromatic spices, look out for the vibrant colours and excited queues and then join in!

An affordable and mouthwatering menu of shawarmas, tagines and boureks are brought to life in front of your eyes with an expertise and a smile.

For vegetarians and meat lovers alike, allow Leeds' new favourite street food stall to revive your lunchtimes with a taste of the exotic!

CANDLEBAR

BAR & RESTAURANT | GRANARY WHARF

Candle House, Granary Wharf
LS1 4GJ

MONDAY - WEDNESDAY | 12:00 - 23:30
THURSDAY - SATURDAY | 12:00 - 24:00
SUNDAY | 12:00 - 23:30

0113 244 6655
www.candlebarleeds.co.uk

WHY NOT TRY?

Get A Pizza The Action – any 2 pizzas from the originals board for £15 – All day Monday – Wednesday.

INTIMATE VENUE SERVING 14 CRAFT KEG BEERS AND OVER 20 PREMIUM WINES

You'll find Candlebar at the far end of Granary Wharf where the towpath of the Leeds Liverpool Canal begins.

Candlebar's food offering of rustic pizza, gourmet sharing boards, selection of salads and desserts will surely satisfy any appetite. From craft keg beers to fine wine served by the glass, premium spirts, a choice of bespoke cocktails and of course Ossett Brewery's own cask beers, there will be something to suit every taste.

Love wine? Once a month Candlebar hosts an evening of tutored tasting with a specialist wine guru. Enjoy a range of wine samples and a lovely selection of nibbles with a ticketed price of only £12.50 per person.

CARAVANSERAI

RESTAURANT | CITY CENTRE

CARAVANSERAI

1 Crown Street
LS2 7DA

MONDAY - THURSDAY | 10:30 - 23:00
FRIDAY | 07:30 - 02:00
SATURDAY | 10:30 - 02:00

0113 234 1999
caravanseraileeds.co.uk

WHY NOT TRY?

Any of Caravanserai's dishes - the spices are exciting, the meats are marinated, the veggie options plentiful.

AUTHENTIC OTTOMAN STREET FOOD FOR THE URBAN EXPLORER

Caravanseri is a place to meet, eat, refresh and reflect. Like Caravnserai, your journey is long, and they know you will relish the chance to pause and gain sustenance, in the perfect meeting place for traders, travellers, and urban nomads.

Caravanserai reflects the culture that grew out of the mists of medieval Mediterranean culture and spread across continents, weaving spice routes and caravan trails. It is an aromatic settlement of flavours, tastes, heady smells and dramatic culinary theatre.

CASA MIA

RESTAURANT | CHAPEL ALLERTON

10 - 12 Stainbeck Lane
LS7 3QY

MONDAY - THURSDAY | 08:00 - 22:30
FRIDAY - SATURDAY | 08:00 - 23:00
SUNDAY | 08:00 - 22:00

0113 266 1269
www.casamiaonline.com

WHY NOT TRY?

Join us for coffee , a meal or take away freshly made cakes, pasta dishes and salads from our delicatessen.

A SMALL SLICE OF ITALY...

Lovingly named the "Coffee Shop" by owners Marta, Francesco and the team, Casa Mia can be all things to all people – cafe bar, pasta bar, wine bar, delicatessen, takeaway, pizzeria or simply just a great restaurant!

Perfect for a variety of occasions, Casa Mia is the ideal spot for an informal breakfast, mid-morning coffee, quick lunch or indulgent dinner - all rounded off with Chapel Allerton's Italian 'cafe' atmosphere.

The smell of the tomato sauce... the freshly ground coffee... the wine corks popping... Casa Mia is a small slice of Italy in North Leeds that will transport you to Florence, Rome or Naples in a heartbeat!

CHA LOUNGE

CAFÉ & BAR | CITY CENTRE

24 Dock Street
LS10 1JF

MON | 10:00 - 16:00 **TUE - WED** | 08:00 - 20:00
THU - FRI | 08:00 - 23:00 **SAT** | 10:00 - 23:00
SUN | 10:00 - 16:00

0113 242 4532
info@chalounge.com

WHY NOT TRY?

Our unique Cha Lounge Curritos or Champagne Afternoon Tea with an Indian twist.

ECLECTIC AMBIENT CAFÉ AND BAR

Cha Lounge promotes a truly ethical and carbon neutral ethos by serving carefully chosen food and beverages sourced locally and globally, from sustainable, fair trade communities. Our aim is to cultivate a feeling of well-being and escapism, while contributing to a fairer society. Community and social justice are at the heart of what we do with 10% of our profits going to charities.

Our menu comprises of delicious fusion food, made from high quality ingredients, matched with organic wines and beers. We have a selection of freshly baked cakes, including gluten free treats. We also have a wide selection of fair-trade leaf teas, from chai to rooibos. Our smoothies & juices are made with nutrient retaining equipment & we have a wide range of juice boosters.

CRANBERRY

CAFÉ | OTLEY

61 Kirkgate
LS21 3HN

MONDAY - FRIDAY | 08:30 - 16:30
SATURDAY | 08:00 - 16:30
SUNDAY | 10:00 - 14:00

01943 851 340

WHY NOT TRY?

Slow roasted in house pulled pork wrap with BBQ sauce and onions and their famous caramel shortbread.

FRESH FOOD, MADE BY PEOPLE WHO CARE

At Cranberry they provide a friendly place to sit and enjoy the best coffee in the area, or you could choose from their selection of teas, or hot chocolate made with chocolate drops steamed with milk and served with (or without) cream and marshmallows.

Cranberry also lovingly make all their sandwiches to order on freshly baked breads. All the cakes are also homemade.

If you are in Otley looking for a friendly place to get something delicious, made by people who care, then Cranberry is the place to head for.

THE CROSS KEYS

PUBLIC HOUSE | CITY CENTRE

107 Water Lane
LS11 5WD

MONDAY - THURSDAY | 12:00 - 23:00
FRIDAY - SATURDAY | 12:00 - 24:00
SUNDAY | 12:00 - 22:30

0113 243 3711
www.the-crosskeys.com

DID YOU KNOW?
Built in 1802, The Cross Keys was frequented by engineer and inventor James Watt, where he reportedly picked up trade secrets from a rival's inebriated workers.

COMBINING CITY STANDARDS WITH COUNTRY APPEAL

Part of the North Bar group, The Cross Keys was named in the Michelin Eating Out in Pubs Guide 2016, was runner up in the Observer Food Monthly's Best Sunday Lunch award 2015, and prides itself on providing the very best quality food, drink and service.

For over ten years, The Cross Keys has been part of the city's up-and-coming Southbank, but step through the doors and you are instantly transported into a country pub that could be miles from anywhere, complete with original beams, roaring fires and cosy alcoves. With one of the best beer gardens in the city, summer at The Cross Keys is a haze of warm afternoons, outdoor barbecues, and cool drinks in the sun.

THE CROWD OF FAVOURS

PUBLIC HOUSE | CITY CENTRE

4-12 Harper Street
LS2 7EA

MONDAY - THURSDAY | 12:00 - 23:00
FRIDAY - SATURDAY | 12:00 - 24:00
SUNDAY | 12:00 - 22:30

0113 246 9405
www.crowdoffavours.co.uk

WHY NOT TRY?

Our delicious Sunday Roasts or join our Burger Club. Or sink into a sofa with a pint and bag of popcorn during the free weekly film nights.

AN AMAZING PUB WITH QUALITY FOOD, MUSIC AND COMEDY

Just off Kirkgate, the oldest street in Leeds, The Crowd of Favours is a great place to kick back and relax while sampling the extensive drinks range and quality fresh food.

There are plenty of little areas set off the main bar which are great for private hire, or if you have a bigger party the cellar bar downstairs with it's red brick walls, comfy sofas and Leeds' smallest private bar could be the perfect venue. In contrast to the cellar space, the pub's small but perfectly formed 'secret' garden is a chilled out space to while away an afternoon with a cold beer in hand.

Also, don't forget to look out for the local artists who cover the walls - literally.

CRUST & CRUMB

CAFÉ | CHAPEL ALLERTON

110B Harrogate Road
LS7 4NY

MONDAY - SATURDAY | 08:00 - 18:00

0113 2680098
www.crustandcrumbbakery.co.uk

WHY NOT TRY?

The Full English, lunch of a platter, salad or gourmet sandwich.

THE PLACE FOR GREAT COFFEE AND GOOD QUALITY FOOD

Born out of a desire to give folk something better, Crust & Crumb promises good quality food, made fresh on site and served up in their beautiful shop.

They do amazing cakes and great lunch options and light bites. There is so much more to be found here, with delicious breakfasts, fresh bread, pastries, sausage rolls and seasonal gourmet sandwiches made with freshly baked bread.

Try the coffee it's barista quality - and if you can't get away from the office, order it in.

DOCK 29

RESTAURANT / BAR | CITY CENTRE

DOCK 29

The Boulevard Dock, The Boulevard
LS10 1PZ

WEDNESDAY & THURSDAY | 10:00 - 21:00
FRIDAY | 10:00 - 22:00 | **SATURDAY** | 10:00 - 18:00
SUNDAY | 12:00 - 17:00

0113 322 6377
www.dock29.co.uk

WHY NOT TRY?

The Breakfast of Champions!

INNOVATIVE AND UNIQUE RESTAURANT/BAR AT LEEDS DOCK

An innovative and unique space created for Leeds, Dock 29 is a restaurant/bar with a big personality. A suspended aeroplane, re-purposed mannequins and retro skis set the scene for an urban food and drink venue jam-packed with events and activity.

Dock 29 is an independent bar brought to you by Leeds Dock and Chilled Events, and is the first day-to-evening bar to open at Leeds Dock. With an impressive food and drink menu, regular games nights, quiz evenings and food feasts it's fast creating the beginnings of a community down at this new waterside neighbourhood.

ECCO PIZZERIA

ITALIAN RESTAURANT | HEADINGLEY

93 Otley Road
LS6 3PS

MON | CLOSED | **TUE - WED** | 17:00 - 23:00
THU | 12:00 - 15:00 & 17:00 - 23:00
FRI - SUN | 12:00 - 23:00

0113 278 2828
www.eccopizzeria.co.uk

WHY NOT TRY?

Pizzas From Around The World; reserving the traditional & facilitating the contemporary has led to new flavour combinations.

THE BEST NEAPOLITAN PIZZA IN LEEDS? YOU DECIDE!

Ecco are proud to serve you the most authentic Neapolitan Pizza & Gelato this side of Naples.

This pizzeria have gone to extreme lengths to ensure that this is the case. Ecco had the oldest wood fired oven makers from Naples come and build their oven and they even recruited a 3rd generation Pizzaiolo (master pizza chef) and searched the length and breadth of Italy to find the most amazing Fior Di Latte, Buffalo Mozzarella, San Marzano tomatoes and flour.

They feel this has resulted in the most amazing easily digestible authentic option imaginable.

EL BARETO

El Bareto

SPANISH RESTAURANT | CHAPEL ALLERTON

120 Gledhow Valley Road
LS17 6LX

MONDAY - SATURDAY | 17:30 - 24:00
SUNDAY | CLOSED

0113 266 6946
www.elbareto.co.uk

WHY NOT TRY?

Their selection of Ribera del Duero, the Spanish earthy red that goes so beautifully with both meat and fish dishes.

A LITTLE PIECE OF AUTHENTIC SPAIN

Chapel Allerton's very own little piece of Spain: enjoy that holiday feeling at the only truly authentic, family-run tapas restaurant in Leeds.

The home-made feel and cosy atmosphere, coupled with hand-picked Spanish wines and traditional recipes from Andalusia to Galicia provide the perfect venue for just a drink and chat after work, a romantic dinner for two, eating out with friends or any special occasion.

FRIENDS OF HAM

BAR & CHACUTERIE | CITY CENTRE

4-8 New Station Street
LS1 5DL

MONDAY - WEDNESDAY | 12:00 - 23:00
THURSDAY - SATURDAY | 12:00 - 24:00
SUNDAY | 12:00 - 22:00

0113 242 0275
www.friendsofham.com

WHY NOT TRY?

A taster board of two meats and two cheeses - wash them down with a guest ale or two! Then relax and a play a little shuffle board.

QUALITY CHARCUTERIE, CHEESE, CRAFT BEER AND FINE WINE

Friends of Ham, is a bar and charcuterie situated in the heart of Leeds. A continental-style café bar that has been recently named the Best Place to Drink in the UK in The Observer Food Monthly Awards 2014.

A bespoke venue offering a British take on the European tapas scene and strong café culture.

Specialising in Italian and Spanish cured meats, the finest cheeses from around the world, sherry and wine; and serving an extensive range of craft beer with 14 taps and over 150 bottles.

In the Ilkley area? You can also visit : 8 Wells Road, Ilkley LS29 9JD

GEORGE & JOSEPH

CHEESEMONGER | CHAPEL ALLERTON

George & Joseph

CHEESEMONGERS

1C Regent Street
LS7 4PE

MONDAY | CLOSED
TUESDAY - SATURDAY | 09:00 - 18:00
SUNDAY | CLOSED

0113 345 0203
www.georgeandjoseph.co.uk

WHY NOT TRY?

Leeds Blue - an award-winning blue cheese made by local cheesemaker Mario Olianas

LEEDS' ONLY SPECIALIST CHEESEMONGER

We are Leeds' only specialist cheesemongers, and opened our shop in Chapel Allerton in 2013. We source and stock the finest locally produced Yorkshire cheeses, along with a selection of the best cheeses from the UK and further afield. We also sell a range of chutneys, biscuits, wines and Yorkshire ales.

We also offer bespoke gift hampers, cheese selections and celebration cakes, as well as other cheese related accessories and gifts.

We host regular tasting events at our shop in Chapel Allerton, and are also available to host corporate and social tasting events.

GRAZE

CAFÉ | CITY CENTRE

43 Call Lane
LS1 7BT

MONDAY - FRIDAY | 08:00 - 15:00
SATURDAY- SUNDAY | CLOSED

0113 245 0295
www.grazeleeds.co.uk

WHY NOT TRY?
Homemade breads, pastries, cakes, soups, salads or stew. Graze also roast their own meats, use free range and serve damn good coffee too.

TOP QUALITY BAKEHOUSE, SERVING HOMEMADE & WHOLESOME FOOD

Serving some of the best breakfasts and lunches one could want. What started as a takeaway sandwich shop has become so much more. With an in-house bakery, relaxing dining room and an outdoor patio area coming soon.

A unique approach making everything in their kitchen, Graze are committed to bringing the best homemade food to their customers, whether in the shop or out, for event and business catering.

THE HOP LEEDS

BAR | CITY CENTRE

The Dark Arches, Granary Wharf
LS1 4BR

MONDAY - SUNDAY | 12:00 - 24:00

0113 243 9854
www.thehopleeds.co.uk

WHY NOT TRY?
Choose any pie, add mash, some boozy beer infused peas or baked beans, gravy & a pint of Ossett Brewery Session Beer, tea or coffee for ONLY £5.

A REAL ALE HOUSE WITH A CONTEMPORARY TWIST

Nestled within the canalside setting of Granary Wharf, you'll find an Ossett Brewery traditional real ale house with a contemporary twist.

We boast 12 handpulls, craft keg beers, real cider as well as the usual main stream favourites. With our purpose built stage area, The Hop Leeds has a real intimate atmosphere for live music.

Every Tuesday from 8pm test your brain skills at the best quiz night in Leeds and who knows you may even win a gallon of ale. With free entry and complimentary supper, what's stopping you?

The Pie Hole at The Hop serves only the best quality and finest tasting pies around. Indulge in the multi award-winning pies of Andrew Jones of Huddersfield.

HOUSE OF KOKO

CAFÉ | CHAPEL ALLERTON

62 Harrogate Road
LS7 4LA

MONDAY - FRIDAY | 08:00 - 18:00
SATURDAY | 09:00 - 17:00
SUNDAY | 10:00 - 16:00

0113 262 1808
www.houseofkoko.com

WHY NOT TRY?

Koko's monthly pop-up restaurants. Up and coming chefs deliver a taster menu of their design.

A UNIQUE COFFEE & TEA HOUSE WITH CREATIVE FOOD

Situated in Chapel Allerton, Leeds, House of Koko is the brain-child of Shanshan Zhu and Chris Ball. A properly independent coffee and tea house that sells Leeds' very own North Star coffee, a selection of premium loose teas and healthy, seasonal food. Not forgetting the cake bar stocked with delicious and curious cakes to make the driest mouth water.

Expect a seasonal menu of plates, platters and paninis that you might not expect from a traditional coffee shop.

Everyone is welcome in Koko. Families, babies, people looking for a place to work and even dogs.

IBÉRICA

RESTAURANT | CITY CENTRE

Hepper House, 17A East Parade
LS1 2BH

MONDAY - SATURDAY | 11:30 - 23:00
SUNDAY | 12:00 - 16:00

0113 403 7007
www.ibericarestaurants.com

WHY NOT TRY?

A deli & wine bar, round the back of Hepper House, offering the best in light bites and delectable Spanish wines.

AUTHENTIC SPANISH CUISINE IN ONE OF THE CITY'S FINEST BUILDINGS

Located in the beautiful Grade II listed Hepper House, Iberica brings a taste of Spain to Leeds.

Iberica's food and drink is sourced from the best Spanish suppliers, from the likes of its Ibérico ham, to its Manchego cheese and Octopus a la gallega, while its drinks menu offers an incredible range of wines exclusive to Iberica and an extensive selection of cocktails and sherries.

As well as the restaurant, which is set under a jaw dropping skylight, Ibérica has a private room for functions and a cocktail bar and lounge. With a menu created by executive chef Nacho Manzano, who has translated his Michelin-star style into casual tapas, set against the rich colonial interiors, Ibérica is the perfect backdrop for any occasion.

KAPOW COFFEE

ESPRESSO BAR | CITY CENTRE

44 The Calls
LS2 7EW

MONDAY - FRIDAY | 07:30 - 16:00
SATURDAY | 09:00 - 16:00
SUNDAY | CLOSED

Kapowcoffee@icloud.com

WHY NOT TRY?

Try one of our tasty toasted Ham and Cheese Croissants.

SERVING GREAT COFFEE DOWN ON THE CALLS

We serve coffee from our favourites La Bottega Milanese and North Star Coffee Roasters. Food is from quality local producers. Stockists of whole coffee beans from North Star, Dark Woods and Baytown.

We're constantly looking for new exciting things for our customers. This summer we are the first to bring refreshing delicious Nitro Cold Brew coffee from Artemis Brew.

KIRKSTALL BRIDGE INN

PUBLIC HOUSE | KIRKSTALL

12 Bridge Road
LS5 3BW

OPENING HOURS

SUN - THU | 12:00 - 23:30
FRI - SAT | 12:00 - 00:30

KITCHEN HOURS

MON - THU | 12:00 - 15:00
& 17:00 - 21:00
FRI & SAT | 12:00 - 21:00
SUN | 12:00 - 17:00

0113 278 4044 www.kirkstallbridge.co.uk

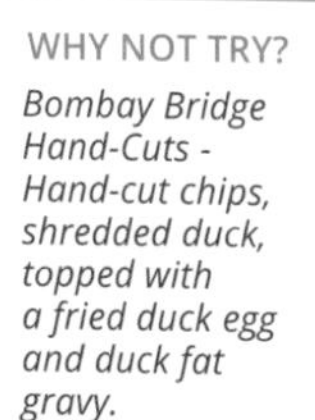

WHY NOT TRY?

Bombay Bridge Hand-Cuts - Hand-cut chips, shredded duck, topped with a fried duck egg and duck fat gravy.

EAT, DRINK AND BE GRATEFUL

A beer hub in suburban Leeds and twice Leeds Pub of the Year. The Kirkstall Bridge Inn holds a wealth of quality cask and craft offerings, from their very own Kirkstall range to craft beers from far flung regions around the globe.

The kitchen serves great contemporary British cuisine whilst taking inspiration from our international beer-loving ethos. Freshly rolled stone baked pizzas, properly crafted sandwiches and deli selections complement our modern pub menu.

LA BOTTEGA MILANESE

ESPRESSO BAR | CITY CENTRE

2 Bond Court
LS1 2JZ

MONDAY - FRIDAY | 07:00 - 18:00
SATURDAY | 09:00 - 18:00
SUNDAY | 10:00 - 17:00

0113 243 1102
www.labottegamilanese.co.uk

WHY NOT TRY?

The Friday Doughnut: fresh home-made 'Zeppole' are delivered on site. Pair this with a traditional 5oz Cappuccino, for an Italian Colazione.

MILAN COFFEE CULTURE: METROPOLITAN HANG OUT

On the Leeds coffee & grub scene since 2009, hell bent on great coffee & promoting the continental social life. Fresh ciabattas, Italian cakes, homemade pastas & soon alcohol at both of their sites.

Based on a simple model of 'if it's not from Milan, then it's from Yorkshire', their own custom Classica blend is roasted here in Yorkshire, milk by Organic Dales, veg by Leeds Markets & bread by the Leeds Bread Co-op.

La Bottega Milanese have two stores in Leeds: The Light [later opening hours] & Bond Court [just behind HSBC on Park Row].

THE LAKESIDE CAFÉ

CAFÉ | ROUNDHAY

Roundhay Park
LS8 2JL

MONDAY - FRIDAY | 10:00 - 17:00
SATURDAY | 09:30 - 17:00
SUNDAY | 10:00 - 17:00

0113 265 7338
www.thelakesidecafe.co.uk

WHY NOT TRY?

Our Loyalty Card System - Raise 5 points for every £1 spent, which can be redeemed on any cafe item!

VIBRANT BUSTLING CAFÉ IN BEAUTIFUL LEEDS PARK

Enjoy some of our exceptionally popular coffee provided by 'United Coffee', alongside one of our wonderfully appealing 'Kitchen Specials', finished off with one of our freshly baked scones.

Regardless of the time of year, The Lakeside Cafe and Roundhay Park is a wonderful place to visit. Lakeside treat every customer, regular and new, in the same welcoming manner every single day.

Become part of Lakeside.

LAYNES ESPRESSO

ESPRESSO BAR | CITY CENTRE

16 New Station Street
LS1 5DL

MONDAY - FRIDAY | 07:00 - 19:00
SATURDAY | 09:00 - 18:00
SUNDAY | 10:00 - 17:00

07828 823 189
www.laynesespresso.co.uk

WHY NOT TRY?

A taste of Laynes coffee and cake inside The Belgrave Music Hall. Also check their website for info on pop up brunch events across Leeds.

CRAFTED COFFEE & FOOD IN THE CITY CENTRE

Since opening in 2011, Laynes has become known across the city for delivering consistency and quality in every food and drink item it has served.

With a high level of customer service given by hugely knowledgeable staff, Laynes is regarded as the 'go-to' place in the city centre for much more than a cup of coffee. Classes are held in the shop after hours for those who want even more knowledge, and a chance to use the top end equipment used by Laynes baristas day in day out.

LAZY LOUNGE

BAR | CITY CENTRE

LAZY LOUNGE

West Point, Wellington Street
LS1 4JY

MONDAY - THURSDAY | 11:00 - 23:00
FRIDAY | 11:00 - 24:00 **SATURDAY** | 12:00 - 24:00
SUNDAY | CLOSED (Available for private hire)

0113 244 6055
www.lazy-lounge.com

WHY NOT TRY?

The weekly gin or wine tastings. Or on the first Thursday of every month, try a whisky tasting with The Yorkshire Fellowship of The Still.

A LEEDS EMPORIUM FOR GIN, WHISKY & WINE

Opened primarily as a wine bar, wine will always remain a major passion. Lazy Lounge are supremely proud of their award winning wine list and the privilege of offering excellent wines.

As they have grown, so has their passion for an abundance of multiple offerings. Though our key affections appear to lie with wine, gin & whisky, a plethora of spirits, cocktails, beers and ciders also feature proudly across their back bar.

Lazy Lounge pride themselves on sourcing the eclectic and simply brilliant. They also particularly enjoy the repartee of recommendations from custom.

LS6 CAFÉ

RESTAURANT | HYDE PARK

14 - 16A Headingley Lane
LS6 2AS

MONDAY - SUNDAY | 09:00 - 23:00
BRUNCH SERVED | 09:00 - 16:00
DINNER SERVED | 17:00 - 21:00

0113 294 5464
www.ls6cafe.com

WHY NOT TRY?

The Best Huevos Rancheros Outside of Mexico - add chorizo for £1.50, yum! LS6 also have live music every Wednesday in the name of jazz!

QUIRKY, FUN, EVENTS SPACE, CAFE, BAR & RESTAURANT

LS6 is a relaxed and quirky café with brilliant décor, which has won them many fans and regular customers from the area around Hyde Park, Leeds.

Their food is as locally sourced as possible, homemade and cooked fresh on site each day.

LS6 are known for their breakfast but pop in and try their dinner menu and homemade cakes too!

The café also has a wide range of continental beer and ale that change frequently, as well as wines, cocktails and great smoothies and milkshakes.

MARVIN'S PIZZA PARLOUR

PIZZERIA & BAR | CITY CENTRE

Arena Quarter, Merrion Way
LS2 8BT

MONDAY - FRIDAY | 12:00 - 14:30 & 17:00 - 22:00
SATURDAY | 12:00 - 22:00
SUNDAY | CLOSED

0113 887 7281
www.marvinspizzaparlour.co.uk

WHY NOT TRY?

One of our 20 bottled beers or cocktails from our extensive list to go with your freshly cooked pizza

A HAVEN FOR PIZZA-LOVERS

Founded in April 2016, Marvin's Pizza Parlour is an all you can eat pizza and salad bar, located in the area of the city centre surrounding the Merrion Centre and close to Leeds' First Direct Arena.

For just £7 at lunchtimes and £12 on evenings, you can indulge in as much delicious pizza and fresh salad as you wish! With a motown soundtrack, great selection of cocktails and milkshakes on offer, this place is sure to become a favourite haunt for many.

With children being half price, this is an ideal place for families with little ones, groups of friends and parties, with outdoor seating, as well as table service. Walk-ins are welcome and no booking is needed!

MEATLIQUOR LEEDS

RESTAURANT | CITY CENTRE

Trinity Centre, Bank Street
LS1 5AT

MONDAY - THURSDAY | 12:00 - 24:00
FRIDAY - SATURDAY | 12:00 - 01:00
SUNDAY | 12:00 - 23:00

0113 843 6090
www.meatliquor.com/leeds

DID YOU KNOW?
As well as restaurants in Marylebone, Covent Garden, Shoreditch, Brighton, Brixton & Leeds, there's also a radio station & a book: find out more online.

BURGERS & DOGS, COCKTAILS & BEERS

MEATliquor Leeds is the sixth venue in the MEATliquor family.

The signature burger, The Dead Hippie, should be your first port of call, followed by the gloriously sticky Monkey Fingers.

Vegetarians aren't left wanting either, with the Halloumi & Mushroom burger featuring in The Evening Standard's round-up of its top five veggie burgers.

MEATliquor are also famous for their cocktails but don't overlook the wide range of beers and ciders both on tap and in cans. Come. Eat. Drink. Dance.

MOMENTS COFFEE

CAFÉ | CITY CENTRE

8 Swinegate
LS1 4AG

MONDAY - FRIDAY | 07:30 - 17:30
SATURDAY - SUNDAY | 09:00 - 16:30

0113 244 6818

WHY NOT TRY?

A homemade cake with your coffee or their house brown sauce on your brekkie. Or, Moments best selling tea; home-made ginger and lemon.

GREAT BREAKFAST & LUNCH CAFÉ IN LEEDS

Moments is a family-run independent café located in Leeds city centre and is a short walk from the train station. Moments has been breaking your regular cafe image for over a year now.

You won't find any typical bacon or sausage butties here - instead you'll fall in love with their home-made fruity brown sauce complimenting a traditional BLT sandwich, twist on English breakfast with farm sourced Toulouse sausages or with home-made bacon bean stew and much more cooked to order for breakfast and lunch.

MONSIEUR DÉJEUNER

CAFÉ | HEADINGLEY

15 North Lane
LS6 3HG

MONDAY - SATURDAY | 09:00 - 18:00
SUNDAY | 10:00 - 16:30

07481 188 264
www.monsieurdejeuner.com

WHY NOT TRY?

A savoury crêpe with a choice of delicious gourmet or homemade fillings

FRENCH TASTE, GREAT FOOD FOR A FRIENDLY PLACE!

Monsieur Déjeuner is a friendly café/crêpe shop with a French taste in the very heart of Headingley. We offer a selection of tasty food and drinks prepared everyday with the best choice of quality products to eat in or to takeaway.

Monsieur Déjeuner is taking you away from the normal and bringing you into France with our food, but with it we are believers in supporting locally sourced produce from Yorkshire. Step into our shop and you can take a little getaway into French life and relax peacefully from the normal routine - without the bad reputation of the traditional French waiter!

MR NOBODY

RESTUARANT & BAR | CITY CENTRE

163 Lower Briggate
LS1 6LY

TUESDAY - THURSDAY | 12:00 - 23:00
FRIDAY - SATURDAY | 12:00 - 01:00
SUNDAY | 12:00 - 22:00

0113 246 7013
www.mrnobody.co.uk

WHY NOT TRY?

A handcrafted cocktail after work with a couple of sociable tapas

THE NEW COOL DESTINATION FOR FRESH FOOD AND VIBES

The old unit that housed Rare has had a complete rehaul and moved into smaller tapas dishes, whilst still maintaining it's larger than life personality and attention to detail.

The new eye catching bar serves cocktails, wines, craft beers and a huge array of spirits to suit all. An ever evolving menu promises exceptional quality in tune with the season.

Many of the staff are known on the local music scene so expect to find an eclectic taste on the music front.

There is also a lovely outdoor space open all year round, for those wishing to enjoy a meal or drinks with friends outside.

THE MUSTARD POT

The Mustard Pot

PUB & RESTAURANT | CHAPEL ALLERTON

20 Stainbeck Lane
LS7 3QY

SUNDAY - WEDNESDAY | 11:00 - 23:00
THURSDAY | 11:00 - 24:00
FRIDAY - SATURDAY | 11:00 - 01:00

0113 269 5699
www.themustardpot.com

WHY NOT TRY?

Dropping in for an event or special occasion and settle down with one of their famous pies or Sunday roasts!!

A TRADITIONAL PUB WITH A GREAT COMMUNITY SPIRIT

The Mustard Pot believe in serving great locally sourced seasonal fresh food and also have a superb range of cask ales which frequently change, showcasing the best of regional breweries such as Banks of West Midlands, Jennings of Cumbria, Wychwood of Oxfordshire and Ringwood micro brewery Hampshire as well as a wide range of premium spirits, bottled beers and wines.

The pub is open seven days a week, serving lunch and dinner and their famous Sunday roasts and a popular quiz is held on Sunday evenings with a strong following.

NORTH BREWING CO.

TAP ROOM | SHEEPSCAR

Taverner's Walk Estate, Sheepscar Grove
LS7 1AH

FRIDAY | 16:00 - 22:00
SATURDAY | 14:00 - 22:00

0113 345 3290
www.northbrewing.com

WHY NOT TRY?

The brewery tap is available for private events and has already hosted a secret gig, work parties, DJs, birthdays and private tours with beer tastings.

THE CLOSEST, FULLY OPERATIONAL BREWERY TAP TO THE CITY CENTRE

North Brewing Co opened in November 2015 and was set up by the teams behind the North Bar group & Belgrave Music Hall-Headrow House. The dream team of hospitality pioneers of speciality beers and proven operators and events organisers also include brewing experts Seb Brink of Golden Owl and Darius Darwel of Bristol Beer Factory.

The brewery and tap offer the exclusive opportunity to try new beers before they reach any bars or pubs, and are situated on the fast developing North Street trail that includes Shuffledog, The Reliance and The Brunswick.

NORTHERN BL°C

ICE CREAM MAKERS | ARMLEY

NORTHERN
—BL°C—

Unit 14, Castleton Close
LS12 2DS

MONDAY - FRIDAY | 08:30 - 17:30

0113 320 6656
www.northern-bloc.com

WHY NOT TRY?

If you'd like to know more and want to sample some ice cream, get in touch

STRAIGHT TALKING ICE CREAM. NOTHING ARTIFICIAL. JUST GREAT INGREDIENTS

At Northern Bl°c our philosophy is based on the simple principle of delivering the highest quality & taste using only the best, responsibly sourced natural ingredients. Served alone or paired with other food and drink, ice cream is equally sublime and it deserves to be honoured and celebrated.

We're not based on the concept of "farmhouse dairy" ice cream nor are we attempting to save the world scoop by scoop. Instead we aim to produce an ice cream experience that is second to none.

Our chef is a world championship winning, third generation ice cream expert so make sure your next ice cream fix is a Northern Bl°c one.

NORTHERN MONK

TAP ROOM | CITY CENTRE

The Old Flax store, Marshall Street
LS11 9YJ

MONDAY - FRIDAY | 08:00 - LATE
SATURDAY - SUNDAY | 10:00 - LATE

0113 243 6430
www.northernmonkbrewco.com

WHY NOT TRY?

Coming down to Northern Monk on a Sunday to try their game specials.

BREWERY, TAP ROOM, BOTTLE SHOP & KITCHEN

The Refectory at their brewery is where they work, rest and play and Northern Monk welcome you to join them.

The tap room features 20 draft beers and an extensive bottle selection, showcasing the beer they brew on site as well as special guests from the North and beyond.

The chefs in the Refectory Kitchen serve up a range of modern, seasonal British dishes from brunch through to dinner.

They also hold a variety of events and the space is available for private functions as well as arranging brewery tours, tastings and open brew days.

NOURISH

CAFÉ | CITY CENTRE

31 Bond Street
LS1 5BQ

MONDAY - SATURDAY | 07:30 - 18:30
SUNDAY | 09:00 - 16:00

0113 243 8249
www.nourishrestaurants.co.uk

WHY NOT TRY?

Eggs No Toast for breakfast. The low carb option - free range eggs, spinach, cherry tomatoes, feta cheese, avocado & smoked salmon

HEALTHY, NUTRITIOUS FAST FOOD IN THE CENTRE OF LEEDS

The Nourish brand was created by nutritionist David Stache, personal trainer, Ben Pryor, and chef, Richard Pryor - their goal being to provide towns and cities saturated with the usual, unhealthy, profit-driven fast food outlets with something entirely different. Nourish's offering of 'fast food with a conscience' aims to combat the nutritionally poor convenience food relied upon by many. The freshest ingredients are delivered daily, every meal is made fresh, on-site, each day. All of our eggs are free range, the meat we use is 100% British, and we only work with local suppliers.
Open seven days a week, and serving breakfast, lunch, dinner and dessert, as well as smoothies, hot drinks and snacks, you can sit and enjoy your meal in or order to go.

OPPOSITE CAFÉ

CAFÉ | CITY CENTRE

26 Blenheim Terrace
LS2 9HD

MONDAY - FRIDAY | 08:00 - 18:00
SATURDAY - SUNDAY | 09:00 - 17:00

www.oppositecafe.co.uk

WHY NOT TRY?

Ordering your office catering; Opposite are one of the largest suppliers to Leeds University and now have a professional team for catering.

HOT DRINKS ENTHUSIASTS SINCE 2005

Leeds' first specialty coffee bar opened in 2005 'Opposite' Leeds University. Since then they have expanded to 3 shops: in the Victoria Quarter and up in Chapel Allerton. They are united by an exacting standard of coffee and the friendliest baristas you've ever met.

But they're also good at healthy, honest, homemade food. Opposite make everything from sandwich fillings to soups to cakes in house, and there are no additives or excess sugar and salt in their grub.

As well as this cafe opposite the University, we are also in Victoria Quarter and Chapel Allerton. Pop in for a cuppa and a nice chat!

OUT OF THE WOODS

CAFÉ | CITY CENTRE

Granary Wharf
LS1 4GL

MONDAY - FRIDAY | 07:00 - 16:00
SATURDAY | 08:30 - 16:00
Find a second café at 113 water Lane, LS11 5WD

0113 245 4144
www.outofthewoods.me.uk

WHY NOT TRY?

Yorkshire Roast Ham Sandwich - using local baker Dumouchel fat free bread, with local ham, cheddar, mustard & secret recipe chutney.

BREAKFAST, BRUNCH & LUNCH FROM LOCAL SOURCES

Out of the Woods pride themselves on creating exciting, healthy & delicious food & drinks with an emphasis on using fantastic local suppliers.

Their coffee shops are small, but perfectly formed with a cosy and friendly atmosphere.

Pop in for a guilt free breakfast, a tasty sandwich, fresh juice/smoothie or coffee & home-made cake, to either sit in or take away.

You can also visit :
113 Water Lane, LS11 5WD

PINCHÉ PINCHÉ

MEXICAN RESTAURANT | CHAPEL ALLERTON

116A Harrogate Road
LS7 4NY

TUESDAY - FRIDAY | 18:00 - LATE
SATURDAY | 11:30 - 15:30 & 17:00 - LATE
SUNDAY | 12:00 - 20:00

0113 268 1110
www.pinchepinche.com

DID YOU KNOW?

Lots of Mexican food is gluten free? There are 19 gluten free dishes on their menu to choose from plus a gluten free beer.

GREAT MEXICAN FOOD IN LEEDS

Pinché Pinché are pushing the boundaries of Mexican food in Leeds with an innovative take on traditional dishes. Our tapas menu is ideal to experience the flavours of authentic Mexican cuisine.

We achieve our distinctive taste by using fresh, quality ingredients, imported Mexican chiles, herbs & spices, homemade salsas and soft corn tortillas - a far cry from stuffed wraps doused in sour cream.

Our knowledge gained living in Mexico City is shared in this cosy spot full of vibrant colours and character. A warm welcome and great Mexican food awaits.

PRIMO'S HOT DOGS

RESTAURANT | CITY CENTRE

12A Corn Exchange
LS0 1AB

MONDAY - WEDNESDAY | 09:00 - 18:00
THURSDAY | 09:00 - 21:00

0113 345 8901
www.primodogs.com

WHY NOT TRY?

The Spanish Harlem - large all beef frankfurter generously topped with Primo's chilli, chorizo, pico salsa and sour cream.

ORIGINAL GOURMET HOT DOGS

Located within the fabulous Leeds Corn Exchange, Primo's serve gourmet hot dogs loaded with fresh, original toppings.

Established in 2011, Primo's have opened a further two hot dog joints at The White Rose Centre and Xscape Yorkshire.

It's not just dogs! Primo's also serve first class burgers, and classic USA sandwiches - their Philly Cheese Steak is a must try.

No reservations required.

RED'S TRUE BARBECUE

RESTAURANT | CITY CENTRE / HEADINGLEY

1 Cloth Hall Street
LS1 2HD

MONDAY - THURSDAY | 12:00 - 23:00
FRIDAY | 12:00 - 24:00 **SATURDAY** | 09:00 - 24:00
SUNDAY | 09:00 - 22:00

0113 834 5834
www.truebarbecue.com

WHY NOT TRY?

NSFW Express Lunch: choose from 6 true BBQ dishes, 6.95 including bottomless soft drinks.

LET THERE BE MEAT!

Hungry souls of Leeds, the end of bad barbecue has arrived. Your saviour is here; Red's True Barbecue.

Rejoice in prime cuts of meat smoked low and slow, so glorious that angels weep tears of joy. Behold glazes, rubs and table sauces infused with flavour and worthy of worship.

People of Leeds, fear no more. Let there be meat! Let there be flavour.

Let there be Red's.

Come forth and worship at Call Lane, or Headingley Church of True Barbecue. You're home. You're saved.

ROLAND'S

BAR | CITY CENTRE

ROLAND'S

39 Call Lane
LS1 7BT

MONDAY - THURSDAY | 16:00 - LATE
FRIDAY - SUNDAY | 12:00 - LATE

0113 318 2964

DID YOU KNOW?

Roland's is the only bar on Call Lane with it's own private beer garden and kitchen?

THE SANCTUARY OF CALL LANE

Independent bar on Call Lane, serving proper drinks and good times to the people of Leeds.

Roland's is the only bar on Call Lane with it's own private beer garden and street-food style kitchen, serving the original and best Pizza Fritta in town.

Expect an understated, easy-going atmosphere and a curated selection of local, national and international cask, draught and bottled beers & ciders, proper wines, spirits and cocktails and officially the best Espresso Martini in the city – powered by Leeds' finest coffee blend from La Bottega Milanese.

ROLA WALA

RESTAURANT | CITY CENTRE

Trinity Kitchen
LS1 5AY

MONDAY - SUNDAY | OPENS 11:00

0113 244 4589
www.rolawala.com

WHY NOT TRY?

Goan Pork combo roll with Beetroot Channa Dal. Half meat, half veg - a flavour haemorrhage.

BRITAIN'S MOST FLAVOURSOME STREET FOOD

Inspired by the Kati Rolls of Kolkata, Rola Wala brings the incredible experience of Indian street food to Leeds.

Choose from a fantastic array of spice-fuelled fillings including flame-grilled Coriander Chicken Tikka, vegetarian Beetroot Channa Dal and much more - prepared from the highest quality ingredients, served in either a toasted naan roll or hot box with rice.

Set permanently in the heart of Leeds Trinity Kitchen, Rola Wala is Britain's most flavoursome street food – a stunning combination of India's freshest flavours, rolled into something truly epic!

SHEARS YARD

RESTAURANT | CITY CENTRE

SHEARS YARD

11-15 Wharf Street
LS2 7EH

MONDAY | CLOSED **TUESDAY - FRIDAY** | DINNER
SATURDAY | LUNCH & DINNER
SATURDAY | LUNCH

0113 244 4144
www.shearsyard.com

WHY NOT TRY?

The mid-week Fixed Price menu - Two courses for £14.50 or three for £17.50, plus add a bottle of wine for £10.

FOOD THAT ISN'T AFRAID TO BE ADVENTUROUS

Shears Yard is an award winning independent kitchen and bar in The Calls area of Leeds City Centre.

Located in the industrial setting of a former rope manufacturers, Shears Yard combines an adventurous a la carte menu with friendly service and a relaxed environment.

The restaurant also offers great value, which makes going regularly a real possibility.

With its late licensed large bar area, Shears Yard is renowned for its cocktails. Plus with its own outside terrace, it is the perfect place to enjoy a drink in the summer.

STOCKDALES

RESTAURANT | CITY CENTRE

8 South Parade
LS1 5QX

MONDAY - THURSDAY | 12:00 - 21:30
FRIDAY - SATURDAY | 12:00 - 22:30
SUNDAY | 12:00 - 17:00

0113 204 2460
www.stockdales-restaurant.com

WHY NOT TRY?

Take advantage of the Lunch and Early Evening menus on weekdays before 19:00

MODERN BRITISH DINING FROM THE HEART OF YORKSHIRE

Stockdales of Yorkshire opened its doors in September 2015. Situated on South Parade, it aims to bring together a deep understanding of agriculture and food service to deliver a truly memorable culinary experience.

Boasting three impressive dining areas and an intimate private dining room there is something for every occasion. Downstairs, a dry-aging fridge displays local beef to develop flavour, which is then enhanced by the Josper Grill for a unique taste.

Aside from the number of steak options, including the signature Wagyu, there's a wide variety of other dishes, plus an unforgettable Sunday Roast. With an extensive wine and cocktail list, there is sure to be something to compliment your first class dining experience.

SUKHOTHAI

THAI RESTAURANT | CITY CENTRE

SUKHOTHAI

15 South Parade
LS1 5QS

MONDAY - SUNDAY | 12:00 - 23:00
See website for Chapel Allerton, Headingley and Harrogate restaurant details

0113 242 2795
www.sukhothai.co.uk

WHY NOT TRY?

One of the many 'Signature Dishes' marked on our 200+ dish a la Carte menu, available at all 4 Sukhothai restaurants, for a real taste of Thai cuisine!

A TRUE THAI TREAT

Sukhothai has been proudly serving Yorkshire with the very best, authentic Thai food since 2002. Its mission is simple "to bring the good people of Yorkshire the ever best Thai food experience".

The original Sukhothai nestles proudly in the heart of the thriving north Leeds suburb of Chapel Allerton and was joined in 2007 by a second site, in the equally vibrant suburb of Headingley. By 2010, Sukhothai was open in the spa town of Harrogate, followed by a natural progression into the hustle and bustle of Leeds city centre in 2012, with a flagship site on South Parade.

All this is underpinned by a succession of awards, accolades and critical acclaim over the years, to be one of the finest Thai dining destinations in the region.

THE SUNSHINE BAKERY

BAKERY & TEAROOM | CHAPEL ALLERTON

THE SUNSHINE BAKERY C.A.

182 Harrogate Road
LS7 4NZ

TUESDAY - FRIDAY | 10:00 - 17:00
SATURDAY | 10:00 - 18:00

0113 268 0656

WHY NOT TRY?

Afternoon tea for £12 per person – homemade treats, sandwiches and sausage rolls, finished off with a bottomless teapot or lashings of coffee.

VINTAGE INSPIRED, QUIRKY BAKERY & TEAROOM

A family run independent bakery, situated in Chapel Allerton for the past 5 years. Specialising in locally sourced produce, they also support other local independents.

They offer an array of delectable treats, from cupcakes to patisseries, all baked in store fresh each morning, as well as enticing artisan sandwiches and breakfast options. In 2015 The Sunshine Bakery won the best place to eat in Chapel Allerton, by the Chapel Allerton Residents Association.

On Thursday, Friday and Saturday evenings they hold a bring-your-own-booze supper club from 6.45pm (bookings only), offering 3 courses for £25. They also hold cupcake decorating classes and the bakery is available for private hire.

THARAVADU

RESTAURANT | CITY CENTRE

7-8 Mill Hill
LS1 5DQ

MON - THU | 12:00 - 14:00 & 18:00 - 22:00
FRI - SAT | 12:00 - 14:00 & 17:00 - 22:30

0113 244 0500
www.tharavadurestaurants.com

WHY NOT TRY?

Meen Kootan - Chefs signature fish curry with Paratha.

HOME OF KERALA CUISINE

Tharavadu - The First authentic Kerala Restaurant in Leeds has become one the favourite dining spot of the region in a very short span of time. The following are some of the achievements by Tharavadu:

Best Indian Restaurant - by Oliver Awards 2015.

Recommended in the Michelin Restaurant Guide 2015.

Recommended in the Harden's Guide 2015, 2016.

One of the Top 10 curry houses in UK by Tripadvisor.

Top 10 Indian Restaurant in UK by The Sun - Newspaper.

TONG TONG

DESSERT HOUSE | CITY CENTRE

15 Thornton's Arcade
LS1 6LQ

MONDAY - THURSDAY | 12:00 - 19:00
FRIDAY - SATURDAY | 12:00 - 20:00
SUNDAY | 12:00 - 17:00

www.facebook.com/Tong-Tong-Bubble-Tea f

WHY NOT TRY?

A Homemade traditional dessert from East Asia

AN EMPORIUM OF CHINESE TEAS AND DESSERTS

A surprising array of wonderful homemade desserts from East Asia freshly made daily using a combination of local produce and imported authentic ingredients. Also available is a large selection of teas ranging from bubble teas, flower teas and traditional Chinese and Japanese tea.

A lovely spot to meet friends, with a comfortable upstairs with European seating or choose the upper seating area Chinese style. A great place to enjoy a leisurely catch up with friends. A real little treasure in the heart of the city.

VANILLA ONE

CAFÉ | CITY CENTRE

The Corn Exchange, 42 Call lane
LS1 7BR

MONDAY - SUNDAY | 10:00 - 17:00

0113 345 8901
www.facebook.com/vanillaoneleeds

f

WHY NOT TRY?

Why not try one of our 18 speciality loose leaf Jeeves and Jericho teas

A FABULOUS COFFEE SHOP IN LEEDS' LANDMARK BUILDING

Here at Vanilla One, we do simple things really well and have been doing so since 2012. We provide a wide range of tea and coffee to enjoy while being seated on the concourse, under one of the most iconic and beautifully designed buildings in Leeds.

If you're looking for a quick bite to eat while exploring the many shops surrounding, we have everything from toasted Panini's and Bagels to full English breakfasts. If you've got a sweet tooth we also offer a range of treats and cakes, which are made fresh and locally everyday. We pride ourselves on our 18 speciality loose leaf Jeeves and Jericho teas and our knowledgeable staff who give excellent service everyday.

VICE & VIRTUE

BAR & RESTAURANT | CITY CENTRE

68 - 72 New Briggate
LS1 6NU

COCKTAIL BAR **TUE - SAT** | 17:00 - 03:00
RESTAURANT **WED - SAT** | 17:00 - CLOSED

0113 345 0202
www.viceandvirtueleeds.co.uk

WHY NOT TRY?

The Viced Old Fashioned... Rittenhouse 100 infused with sour cherries, grapefruit, rosemary, vanilla sugar and bitters.

INNOVATIVE BRITISH COCKTAILS

Vice and Virtue is a cocktail lounge and restaurant in the heart of Leeds City Centre's Northern Quarter. The cocktail bar, set on the first floor, offers bespoke cocktails incorporating home-made infusions, syrups, bitters and liqueurs, with the menu based on seasonal produce and is a combination of chef meets mixologist. There are also bottled ales and a fantastic back bar.

The restaurant, located on the second floor, offers brilliant views over Leeds Centre. Created by award winning chef, Luke Downing, the restaurant promises fine dining plates. All dishes have complementing wines, ales, infusions and cocktails, with the menu changing daily. Described as fine dining without the fuss.

VIET GUY

VIETNAMESE RESTAURANT | CITY CENTRE

VIET GUY

159 Lower Briggate
LS1 6LY

MONDAY - SATURDAY | 11:00 - 23:00
SUNDAY | 11:00 - 22:00

0113 345 5430

WHY NOT TRY?

Free delivery to your home or business in LS1 or LS2, for a taste of Vietnam in the form of a takeaway treat

LEEDS' FIRST VIETNAMESE RESTAURANT

Opening in 2015 as the first Vietnamese restaurant in Leeds, Viet Guy serves truly authentic Vietnamese cuisine and is an exciting addition to the independent restaurants found on Lower Briggate.

Both the healthy oriental food and passionate, friendly staff create a memorable dining experience - whether you're eating alone, catching up with friends or with family for a special occasion.

Viet Guy prides itself on being an indulgent haven, offering traditional dishes and a warm atmosphere - once tried it will almost certainly become a regular haunt for many.

WAPENTAKE

CAFÉ / BAR | CITY CENTRE

92 Kirkgate
LS2 7DJ

MONDAY - FRIDAY | 07:30 - 23:00
SATURDAY | 10:00 - 23:00
SUNDAY | 10:00 - 21:00

0113 243 6248
www.wapentakeleeds.com

WHY NOT TRY?

Some of our lovely home baked bread

A LITTLE PIECE OF YORKSHIRE

We are an artisan bakery, cafe & bar dedicated to our love of Yorkshire. It may help you understand us when you understand the name; Besides being divided into three Ridings, East, North and West, Yorkshire was further sub-divided into administrative areas called 'Wapentakes' - the word derived from an assembly or meeting place.

You will find us nesting on Kirkgate, not far from the market where we buy all our produce. There is daily baked bread usually sat by some cake creations, gluten-free & vegan. Besides being a stop off for bacon butties & early morning coffees we are also here to ease you in to the evening. We have an array of spirits including Yorkshire gins, a selection of local keg and cask ales.

WHITELOCK'S

ALE HOUSE | CITY CENTRE

6-8 Turks Head Yard
LS1 6HB

MONDAY - THURSDAY | 11:00 - 24:00
FRIDAY - SATURDAY | 11:00 - 01:00
SUNDAY | 11:00 - 23:00

0113 245 3950
www.whitelocks.com

WHY NOT TRY?

The freshly cooked and locally sourced menu was recently given the thumbs up by the nation's favourite fearsome food critic Jay Rayner.

LEEDS' OLDEST & BEST PUB

Since 1715 Whitelock's has become an integral and much loved piece of the city's fabric.

Located on Leeds' busiest shopping street Briggate, the pub's cosy interior and unique outdoor yard provide a haven of comfort. New ownership has revitalised the atmosphere whilst preserving its historic charm. Expect friendly service of craft beers, real ales, world wines and home cooked food served to cool tunes beneath relaxed chatter.

Welcoming new and old from near and far, Whitelock's is Leeds' must-visit city local.

WHITES

CAFÉ / BAR | HEADINGLEY

WHITES

9 Otley Road
LS6 3AA

MONDAY - SATURDAY | 09:00 - 00:00
SUNDAY | 10:00 - 17:00

0113 328 0668
www.whitescafebar.com

WHY NOT TRY?

...our awesome all day breakfasts.

RELAXED CAFE, BAR AND LIVE MUSIC VENUE

Since opening as a deli in October 2014 Whites has expanded it's menu, opening hours & customer base! A welcomed alternative to the typical student haunts of Headingley; a place to relax with a coffee, cocktail or just get your fix of the all day breakfast.

Whites create and cook all their food in house and pride themselves on a warm welcome. Be sure to get there early on weekends as there's usually a queue out of the door for those eggs Benedict!

You can attend weekly events such as the Wednesday quiz, and live music every Friday and Saturday from 8pm.

THE WHITE SWAN

PUBLIC HOUSE | CITY CENTRE

Swan Street
LS1 6LG

MON - WED | 12:00 - 23:00
THU - FRI | 12:00 - 24:00
SAT | 11:00 - 24:00 **SUN** | 12:00 - 22:30

0113 242 0187
www.whiteswanleeds.co.uk

WHY NOT TRY?

Leeds Best battered Fish and Chips with a pint of Leeds Brewery's infamous Leodis lager

ONE OF BRIGGATE'S MOST FAMOUS ALLEY PUBS

Adjoining the world famous City Varieties and tucked up the Swan Street alley off Briggate.

The White Swan is a great place to escape the busy shopping streets of Leeds. With a freshly prepared menu, locally sourced with regularly changing specials, it's one of the best places to eat in the city centre as well as offering a cool, relaxing space to savour a few drinks.

Enjoy a delicious Sunday Roast accompanied by a Bloody Mary and your favourite board game whilst listening to the in-house live pianist.

WINO

CAFÉ / BAR | CITY CENTRE

69 St. Paul's Street
LS1 2TE

MONDAY | 15:00 - 20:00
TUESDAY & WEDNESDAY | 12:00 - 20:00
THURSDAY & FRIDAY | 12:00 - 21:00
SATURDAY | 15:00 - 21:00

0113 345 5960
www.winoleeds.co.uk

WHY NOT TRY?

...Our lunch offers, any of our food boards with a drink - available to eat in or take away

WINE BAR & MERCHANTS

Hidden gem located in the bustling financial district . A unique selection of wines all available by the glass, cheese, charcuterie and other Mediterranean deli delights with ever changing options.

Along with our wines we serve beers, prosecco and champagnes all available to take away as part of our merchant service.

The personal service, wines and warm welcome lie at the heart of Wino's philosophy along with our fantastic offerings. We provide a comfortable, cosy experience perfect for any occasion.

Our bar is also available for private event hire perfect for networking, meetings and celebrations alike. Packages available.

WOLF STREET FOOD

RESTAURANT | CITY CENTRE

8A St Paul's Street
LS1 2LE

MONDAY - FRIDAY | 07:00 - 15:00

0113 244 9500
www.wolfstreetfood.com

WHY NOT TRY?

Our signature piada's (thin Italian flatbread), filled with spaghettini, marinated meat, homemade sauce and then a selection of salad from our deli counter.

ITALIAN STREET FOOD

At WOLF we bring traditional Italian street food from the carts of Italy to the people of the Leeds. Tapping into the nations love of Italian flavour and giving it a unique modern twist, we pride ourselves in making everything from scratch on site everyday. All our meats are marinated for 24 hrs using Italian fresh herbs and spices and come from our northern butchery. Come visit early in the morning for a strong Italian coffee and a freshly baked croissant and you will see our staff busy chopping, slicing and preparing the lunchtime delights ready to serve the queues!

Try our signature Piada's or salads, focaccia, freshly made pasta or a cheeky stone baked pizza, which are all on offer for you to bespoke to be as healthy or as naughty as you like.

ZAAP

THAI STREET FOOD | CITY CENTRE

Grand Arcade
LS1 6PG

MONDAY - SUNDAY | 11:00 - 24:00

0113 243 2586
www.zaapthai.co.uk

WHY NOT TRY?

*Our dishes marked with **แซ่บ**. These can be made to your taste & we can give them the full Thai street food spice hit for those brave enough to try it!*

LET US TRANSPORT YOU TO THE STREETS OF BANGKOK!

Zaap brings a small corner of Bangkok to the Grand Arcade, in the heart of Leeds' bustling city centre. Yet, Zaap is like no other restaurant before it – if you are lucky enough to have been to Thailand, then you'd be forgiven for thinking you'd left Leeds and had landed right in the middle of a Bangkok street food market!

The menu is as authentic as you would find on Yaowarat Road, in Bangkok, and features around 80 dishes. You'll find popular Thai starters, soups, salads, dim sum style dishes, as well as mouthwatering grilled and roasted meats, spicy curries and many, many more dishes besides.

MUSIC + NIGHTLIFE

PRICK UP YOUR EARS AND PICK UP YOUR FEET...

Leeds is a city with a thousand sound tracks. Whether you're searching for a gig or club night there are an array of independent venues, large and small catering to your needs.

DIGGIN' THE SCENE

by Matt Bradshaw (Jumbo Records), photography by Mike Medlock, illustration by Johnny Cosmic @midnightvipers

Often, whenever I read about a City's music scene, it seems to be framed in one of three lazy ways.... It's either:

1) A hark-back to the mythical glory days of old.

2) An all too obvious list of band and club names aimed at the casual music fan.

3) A poorly disguised exercise in hyping up friends bands and club nights.

These particular overviews hardly lend themselves to pointing anyone to the real deal, and all unfortunately fall flat in enlightening anyone (musician or music-fan alike) about the scene's vibrancy, echoing throughout its many nuanced forms. The thing I like about Independent Leeds and The Little Black Book is that its real beauty is as an enabler, giving us a sneak peek through Leeds' magical map (physical and metaphorical), and pushing EVERYONE into the spotlight shine. So, in a roundabout way, it leaves a space for the reader to explore... and as it grows, in print form and online, you're ever more able to look deeper into whatever you're into, be that music, culture or just plain shopping...

MUSIC IS LOVE

What I've always been drawn to is when people wax lyrical about what a great PLACE cities can be for music, and not just in a geographic way either. Yes, some cities can be full of venues and bands, but it's easy to miss the community around this, and Leeds has a culturally rich and inclusive commonality if you know where to look.

So let's put on the walking shoes and examine why Leeds bubbles with so much great genre-hopping musicality, and while we're at it we should saunter around some of those inspiring streets and maybe dig a little deeper... Firstly, I feel it's no coincidence that Leeds has soooo many record shops, and slinging music and tickets are but one of their magnificent traits, for they also double up as hang-outs for local musicians, DJ's and promoters, enabling them to get their art, music and tickets on sale... just a glance around the walls of places like Jumbo and Crash Records reveal a cornucopia of posters advertising Leeds shows, club-nights, rehearsal studios, jamming sessions, D.I.Y shows, and often showing off the talents of local illustrators and designers like Drew Millward or Dave Tyson. Resting on their counters and floors are sassy selections of free magazines and zines directing people to some seriously great happenings around and about, and manning the shops are staff that certainly know their musical onions enough to recommend bars, clubs and venues that cater musically to whatever your particular peccadilloes may be (and if you're a regular you may even glean info on when and where those future elusive secret guest DJ slots and unmissable epic bands playing tiny venues will be happening).

Playing a grand part of the music scene in Leeds are the club-nights and backrooms, all-dayers and soirees that themselves need an environment in which to thrive, and thankfully we're blessed with a plethora of perfect spaces and places... Take open-minded bars in Leeds like Outlaws Yacht Club or The 212 Bar, whose soaring reputations exist from hosting some of the best international and local DJ's for free. What's intriguing about this arrangement is that they play not so much for the money but for the chance to play to crowds of sonically curious like-minds on superbly constructed sound-systems (and yes, they're BARS not clubs). Other

bars in Leeds such as North Bar or Reliance have created genuinely atmospheric environments by hosting showcases and galleries of local artists and photographers which sit alongside brilliant brews from local breweries and tasty treats from local food suppliers. It's that sizzling connectivity, that (beer)tapping into the BIGGER picture that excites me the most... It works unbelievably well when award-winning venues like The Brudenell, The Key Club or The Belgrave actively foster local talents, giving them the chance to glimmer alongside international artists of repute... and when you look at the listings of most club nights in Leeds you'll more often than not see plenty of local DJ's and producers getting the chance to enhance that superstar booking by warming up the crowds and dropping local labels and bands to eager dancefloors.

For the music fan, this works like an absolute dream, within a week you could check out an Americana or folk legend playing an intimate show at Oporto or The Grove, see Fourtet or Floating Points play a secret set at Cosmic Slop, go see some incredible jazz and funk superstars dazzle at The Wardrobe or Sela Bar, party like it's 1999 at Hifi or Sandinista, jerk like crazy to punk and noise at Wharf Chambers or Temple Of Boom, you name it it's probably happening soon... and if you're a budding musician, DJ, promoter or producer, Leeds lays out a freakishly strong array of; record labels to be signed to like Hide And Seek Records, Come Play With Me and Clue Records, rehearsal rooms to practice in like

Rock And Roll Circus, music shops overflowing with instruments and turntables like Hobgoblin, Northern Guitars or Superfi, custom printers like Awesome Merchandise and Nobrand that'll make your merch-stands trickle over with goodies, recording studios big and small like Eiger Studios in which to formulate that new world conquering release, local radio heaven in the form of KMAH or PEOPLES FM, and of course... all those great spaces and places in which to play or launch your brand new night in.

For Leeds' hyper-active musical community, this is just a small part of the whole... The sheer range of choices brought about by the feverish minds of promoters and venue managers makes it pretty much impossible for me to point you towards a fraction of the action within these four pages, that's for sure, and this lovely approach is the PERFECT conduit, intersecting in a myriad of ways with behemoths like First Direct Arena, Canal Mills or Leeds Festival, through passionate Not For Profits like Leeds Music Scene, Cops and Robbers or Leeds Jazz, it all connects and makes sense somehow, and creates something rather special, bigger than the sum of its parts... The more you look the more you'll find, and with that, all I can say is that I implore you all to explore some more... It'll take a while, trust me...

INSPIRATION IN MOTION

Rheima Robinson, of Leeds Young Authors and Sunday Practise, talks to David Hamilton a founder of Phoenix Dance

Grass roots is a term often used by 'the people' which causes significant ricochet effects through layers of governance, significant changes to the course of a movement forever. Grass roots creates new definitions of faceless monster industries with the act of a man with a soul. Grass roots movements often occur when voices are unrepresented, when tired communities yearn for social, economic or environmental change.

David Hamilton, founder of Phoenix Dance Theatre, told me a short story about having to defend himself against racist taunts. After enduring cruel comments for weeks, David's tolerance finally depleted. The consequences of his actions ran through his mind like death before his eyes but nonetheless, he punched the guy. It was through these late 70s times that David, a Caribbean teenager, created a legacy beyond imagination. Although not a direct reaction to an action, one of Britain's leading dance companies cannot deny its grass roots.

In early 1981, David was asked to lead jazzfunk contemporary dance group Zodiac. In November 1981, the idea of a dance company popped into David's head. With that seed alone, he became one of the youngest artistic directors in the country. It was members of Zodiac that David approached for the delivery of Phoenix.

Himself, Vilmore James and Donald Edwards were the first dancers to represent Phoenix. In February 1982, they did their first official performance at Saint Chads Headingley where they were paid £10. David kept it for 7 months to impress upon himself that this is where he started. "Sometimes you need to know that you can start small and it will grow."

When presented with the idea of a dance company, Charles Gardener, who was head of Intake High and played very important role in

dance and education, suggested to involve Nadine Senior, dance teacher at Harehills, who provided the rehearsal space. It was also Charles who suggested the name Phoenix as David was initially going with a name he now laughs at, 'Artistic Expression'.

Fast forward into 2016, David is an artist. An individual with a multifaceted status. He pursued a solo career with his first show 'Musings'. He has been a movement director for organizations such as Leeds Young Authors. He has found himself acting in the show 'Run Away Diamonds'. He directed Khadijah Ibrahiim's play 'Another Crossing'. He is unrestricted by dance although dance remains his hub.

David calls his personal style "La Reggram Eyerayshun" or reggae/ contemporary. His love of reggae, its roots and principles taught him to be creative and contributed to David's realization of the connections between social dance and folk dance.

It was a similar folk vibe found in reggae that has helped David maintain his relationship with Leeds. Teaching in primary schools, putting on shows such as Carnival Messiah and Kwanza is what has kept him engaged in the city and help the city engage with dance alike. He explains how the dance community has changed, with the Mandela Centre in Chapeltown transformed through the help of Reggae Jazz Contemporary, and The Northern School of Contemporary Dance across the street meaning people now have a chance to be formally trained. "There was a time when these things weren't there and they are here now. That's important."

David is now interested in stabilizing the future of dance in Leeds. Will the dancer's needs be assessed? Where does financial and institutional power leave freelance artists? In relationship to economic trade in this vision, where does it sustainability fit?

51% BOURBON

SPECIALIST BAR | CITY CENTRE

Hirst's Yard
LS1 6NJ

MONDAY - SATURDAY | 16:00 - LATE
SUNDAY - MONDAY | CLOSED

0113 322 9919
www.51percentbourbon.co.uk

WHY NOT TRY?

The happy hour between 4pm and 8pm where you can enjoy 2 for £10 cocktails. Also contact 51% for Bourbon Masterclass dates!

LEEDS' ONLY SPECIALIST BOURBON WHISKEY BAR

51% Bourbon is refreshingly straight forward and unpretentious. As soon as you walk in the rose red lighting, dark wooden tables, chairs and casks combine with the rock 'n' roll backdrop to make you feel like you're in a relaxed log cabin bar in the States.

There's a mammoth selection of 70 bourbons, including normal, small batch and single barrel tipples, and we offer the only bourbon masterclass in Leeds! If bourbon whiskey in the usual form is not your thing, there is an extensive cocktail menu which will show you other ways to enjoy the spirit.

ALFRED'S

BAR | MEANWOOD

Alfred

6 Stonegate Road
LS6 4HY

MON - WED | 17:00 - 23:00 **THU** | 17:00 - 24:00
FRI | 15:00 - 24:00 **SAT** | 13:00 - 24:00
SUN | 13:00 - 03:00

0113 278 0779
www.northbar.com/alfred

DID YOU KNOW?
Alfred was named for the nearby 'King Alfred's Castle' built in 1770 and demolished in the 60s, and after director Alfred Hitchcock.

A LITTLE BAR IN MEANWOOD WITH A BIG SELECTION

Slap bang in the middle of Meanwood, minutes from Meanwood Park, Alfred is the perfect local hang out for fans of great beer, wine and spirits.

Knowledgable and friendly staff take you through the huge range of drinks, surrounded by stylish decor with a 50s twist. Alfred opened in 2011, leading the charge to develop Meanwood's now-thriving, food and drink scene.

A stone's throw from the beautiful Meanwood Park, Alfred is the perfect spot for families, dog-walkers, or anyone just out for a stroll.

THE BACKROOM

BAR | CITY CENTRE

50A Call Lane
LS1 6DT

THURSDAY | 23:00 - 04:00
FRIDAY | 22:00 - 06:00
SATURDAY | 21:00 - 06:00

0113 243 8666
www.thebackroomleeds.co.uk

WHY NOT TRY?

Booking a table; their hosts will meet you on arrival and provide table service so you can enjoy your evening stress free. Packages start from £100.

1920'S SPEAKEASY BAR & EVENT SPACE

Showcasing Leeds' top DJ talent, Backroom play all the classic & contemporary party anthems to keep you dancing until the early hours.

The bar is a large event space in the heart of Leeds City Centre, situated by the Corn Exchange, and just a few minutes walk from the train and bus stations.

The Backroom Leeds is perfect for birthday parties, society events, club nights & socials.

BELGRAVE MUSIC HALL

BAR, MUSIC VENUE & FOOD | CITY CENTRE

1 - 1A Cross Belgrave Street
LS2 8JP

SUNDAY - WEDNESDAY | 11:00 - 24:00
THURSDAY - SATURDAY | 11:00 - LATE

0113 234 6160
www.belgravemusichall.com

DID YOU KNOW?

Belgrave Music Hall host regular street food and art markets? Check their Facebook page for updates and events.

CULTURAL HUB IN THE NORTHERN QUARTER

Located in Leeds' vibrant Northern Quarter, Belgrave Music Hall and Canteen first opened its doors in 1934 as Leeds Children's Palace, a 3-storey recreation hall and nursery.

Spread over three floors the venue comprises two bars, two kitchens, a 250 capacity event space and a spectacular roof terrace.

The Belgrave host live music, film, monthly Street Food events and serve fresh, canteen style food, amazing cask ales and premium craft beers as well as frozen cocktails and a wide range of coffees from Laynes. WIFI is of course, free.

BROOKLYN

BAR | CITY CENTRE

BROOKLYN

50 Call Lane
LS1 6DT

MON | CLOSED
TUE - FRI | 16:00 - LATE
SAT | 12:00 - LATE **SUN** | 16:00 - 01:00

0113 322 9919
www.brooklynbar.co.uk

WHY NOT TRY?

2 for £10 cocktails at all times! Sign up to the website for regular vouchers and promotions.

NEW YORK INSPIRED VENUE ON CALL LANE

Brooklyn on Call Lane is a gem to discover.

Its sleek décor, with nods to New York City, make it a comfortable spot for a cheeky cocktail or bottle of lager, while the eclectic soundtrack of funk, soul, R&B and hip-hop liven it up on an evening.

Brooklyn's ace up their Yankee sleeves is the Kitchen that resides within, dishing up some of the tastiest burgers this side of JFK.

It has an exceptional cocktail menu too, with the Lynchburg Lemonade and Brooklyn Berry Swizzle.

THE BROTHERHOOD OF PURSUITS & PASTIMES

BAR | CITY CENTRE

56 - 58 New Briggate
LS2 8JP

MON - WED | 12:00 - 01:00 **THU** | 12:00 - 02:00
FRI - SAT | 12:00 - 03:00 **SUN** | 12:00 - 24:00

0113 243 4060
www.thhisisthebrotherhood.com

WHY NOT TRY?

Best of British Bar tending cocktails, kindly designed exclusively by some of Leeds' most distinguished tenders of this generation.

FOR GENTLEMEN OF CHARACTER & WOMEN OF SUBSTANCE

The Brotherhood of Pursuits and Pastimes exists to entertain the gentlefolk of Leeds with the finest sporting events and classic drinks, including expertly concocted cocktails and craft beers of distinction. Not to mention artisan pies to die for.

They are no common or garden 'Sports Bar' mind you. They believe that those of taste and character shouldn't leave such attributes at the door. Maintain your standards dear Brothers and Sisters and take in an experience that's as much 'damned fine Bar' as it is 'Sport'.

BRUDENELL SOCIAL CLUB

BAR & VENUE SPACE | HYDE PARK

33 Queen's Road
LS6 1NY

SUNDAY - THURSDAY | 12:00 - 23:30
FRIDAY - SATURDAY | 12:00 - 24:00

0113 275 2411
www.brudenellsocialclub.co.uk

WHY NOT TRY?

Special daytime offers on drinks with prices from £1.80 a pint (12 - 4pm), along with free pool.

LEEDS' TRUE INDEPENDENT SOCIAL AND MUSIC VENUE!

The Brudenell is a lively and fun-loving venue that embraces music and art, under a wide and diverse umbrella that has no boundaries.

It has been a centrepiece of the Leeds music scene for a number of years, hosting gigs most evenings.

Facilities include a lounge, games room, concert room and live sports screenings and we serve quality ales at a fair price.

The Brudenell Social Club is a community 'non profit making' venue in Leeds 6 owned by its members, run by its members, for its members.

CALL LANE SOCIAL

BAR | CITY CENTRE

CALL LANE SOCIAL

38 Call Lane
LS1 6DT

MONDAY - SUNDAY | 17:00 - 04:00

0113 247 0285
www.calllanesocial.co.uk

WHY NOT TRY?

Taking advantage of the free 5-9 cards. Ask at the bar for the cards, there are a range of £2.50 drinks between 5pm and 9pm.

CALL LANE'S FRIENDLIEST BAR

An effortlessly cool hangout dedicated to giving you the warmest welcome on Call Lane.

If you're looking for a friendly bar with a lively atmosphere, good drinks, good music, good people and good times, then Call Lane Social is the place to visit.

Their friendly staff are happy to serve you one of their classic cocktails, or anything from the well stocked back bar or fridges.

Call Lane Social are open 7 days a week and party every night till 4am to a soundtrack of Rock N' Roll, Funk and Soul.

THE DECANTER

WINE BAR | CITY CENTRE

17 Park Row
LS1 5JQ

SUNDAY - WEDNESDAY | 12:00 - 23:00
THURSDAY | 12:00 - 24:00
FRIDAY - SATURDAY | 12:00 - 02:30

0113 222 2222
www.thedecanter.co.uk

WHY NOT TRY?

Their fabulous Charcuterie & Cheese selection! All locally sourced, delicious and the perfect pairing with the extensive wine list!

SOPHISTICATED WINE BAR IN THE HEART OF LEEDS

Wine is the speciality at The Decanter, who use expert wine suppliers to create a wine list to wow the people of Leeds.

You can expect something different, varieties you've maybe never tried, sourced from the finest vineyards from all corners of the world.

Along with the vast selection of wines there are fine champagnes, sparkling wine, premium lagers, craft beers, classic cocktails and spirits. A charcuterie menu is also available, where staff will be happy to suggest the best wine to go with your meal.

THE EAST VILLAGE

BAR | HYDE PARK

47 - 49 Brudenell Grove
LS6 1HR

MONDAY - SUNDAY | 18:00 - 01:00

0113 226 3898
www.theeastvillage.bar

LOOK OUT FOR

East Village's regular happy hours enhancing the good times!

COCKTAIL & MUSIC BAR

An exciting new arrival to the vibrant student-hub, Hyde Park. The East Village brings an artistic edge and casual cool to the area.

This friendly New York style community bar serves individually sourced high-quality cocktails, wines and beers at affordable prices in a stylishly comfortable setting that welcomes both new-comers and locals to relax into the evening with good company and timeless tunes.

There is a vital underground vibe where artists and musicians are openly supported to showcase their talents, and everybody is invited to enjoy The East Village community.

EIGER MUSIC STUDIO

MUSIC STUDIOS | HUNSLET

New Craven Gate
LS11 5NF

MONDAY - SUNDAY | 24/7

0113 244 4105
www.eiger-studios.com

DID YOU KNOW?

Eiger was used for production rehearsals by Damon Albarn's Africa Express, feat. members of Rizzle Kicks, Maximo Park & The Libertines.

REHEARSAL & RECORDING STUDIOS, VENUE AND EQUIPMENT HIRE

Eiger encompasses everything music, providing a central hub for the thriving Leeds music and arts scene.

Located just a few minutes from Leeds city centre, the studios are favoured by bands of all kinds from Yorkshire and beyond, and the 350 capacity venue has been host to some of the biggest names in music.

Rehearsals, recordings, club nights, equipment hire, gigs, parties, events, video/photo shoots, music exams, seminars, workshops, pre-production, auditions... the list goes on! Whatever you need, Eiger can cater for just about anything.

THE FENTON

PUBLIC HOUSE | CITY CENTRE

161 Woodhouse Lane
LS2 3ED

MONDAY - WEDNESDAY | 12:00 - 00:00
THURSDAY | 12:00 - 01:00
FRIDAY & SATURDAY | 12:00 - 02:00
SUNDAY | 15:00 - 23:00

0113 243 1382
www.thefentonleeds.com

WHY NOT TRY?

Life Drawing and Open Mic every Tuesday from 8pm

THE CITY'S LOCAL BOOZER

Once upon a time in a great land, not far from where you are right now, there was a pub like no other. It was the simple things that made this place so special. A great selection of local cask ales, craft ciders, great wines, cocktails and everything else you would expect to find at your local. And some things that may surprise you. All sourced locally to get you locally sauced.

Once your palette is satisfied may your mind be pleased; there's pool and darts, a jukebox, board games and a real life puppy! There are poker nights, jam nights (live music, not for your toast), a most unconventional quiz, life drawing, stand up comedy, improv comedy, art exhibitions, big parties, small parties, garden parties and everything in between.

FURTHER NORTH

BAR | CHAPEL ALLERTON

Further NORTH

194 Harrogate Road
LS7 4NZ

MON - TUE | 17:00 -23:00
WED - THU | 17:00 - 24:00 **FRI** | 15:00 - 24:00
SAT | 13:00 - 24:00 **SUN** | 13:00 - 23:00

0113 237 0962
www.northbar.com/further-north

WHY NOT TRY?

Further North's very own bespoke coffee roasted just for them in collaboration with Laynes Espresso.

WHERE YOUR FRONT ROOM MEETS YOUR FAVOURITE LOCAL

Little sister to the legendary North Bar on New Briggate in the Leeds city centre, it boasts the same commitment to providing the very best beers in the world in a cosy and unpretentious atmosphere.

Further North has regular guest ales from a selection of great English Breweries including Magic Rock, Thornbridge, Ridgeside, Elland, Roosters and Salamander.

Bread, Cheese & Meat Boards are available at all times as well as Laynes Espresso coffee.

HEADROW HOUSE

BAR, RESTAURANT & VENUE | CITY CENTRE

HEADROW HOUSE

Bramleys Yard, 19 The Headrow
LS1 6PU

MONDAY - THURSDAY | 16:00 - 24:00
FRIDAY | 12:00 - 02:00 **SATURDAY** | 11:00 - 03:00
SUNDAY | 11:00 - 23:00

0113 245 9370
www.headrowhouse.com

WHY NOT TRY?

Our Pilsner Urquell - fresh, unfiltered and unpasteurized Czech beer straight from the tank

FOOD, DRINK, EVENTS, ART

Headrow House is a multi use arts and event space comprised of 4 floors featuring a large beer hall with giant communal tables, Redondo Beach cocktail bar on the third floor, 150 capacity music venue and event space, the Ox Club restaurant plus 3 outdoor areas. The fourth outdoor area, Kennedy Meadows, will be opening in 2016.

Each area of Headrow House offers something different, from our Beer Hall selling fresh unpasteurised Czech beer, to our grill restaurant, Ox Club, which is centred around a custom made 'Grillworks' grill imported from Michigan to Redondo Beach, the Miami style cocktail bar.

THE HIFI CLUB

MUSIC & COMEDY CLUB | CITY CENTRE

2 Central Road
LS1 6DE

TUESDAY, WEDNESDAY & FRIDAY | 23:00 - 03:00
SATURDAY | 20:00 - 03:00
SUNDAY | 22:00 - 04:00

0113 242 7353
www.thehificlub.co.uk

DID YOU KNOW?

HiFi used to be known as the 'Leeds Central' back in the 70s?! HiFi still plays host to the 'Central Soul Alldayers' with the original DJ crew!

CLUB NIGHTS, LIVE MUSIC, COMEDY & FILM!

The HiFi Club is an independent venue based in Central Leeds.

Three times winner of both the "Best Nightclub" and "Best Live Music Venue", HiFi is home to long standing events such as Wednesday nights MoveOnUp and The Sunday Joint.

Past guests to grace the stage include Nightmares on Wax, SBTRKT, Little Dragon, Onra, Peanut Butter Wolf and funk legend Marva Whitney.

Also be sure to check out the weekly Saturday night Comedy Sessions and keep an eye out for special events and film screenings throughout the year.

HIRST'S YARD

BAR | CITY CENTRE

15 Hirst's Yard
LS1 6NJ

SUNDAY - MONDAY | CLOSED
TUESDAY - FRIDAY | 16:00 - LATE
SATURDAY | 14:00 - LATE

0113 322 9919
www.hirstsyard.co.uk

WHY NOT TRY?

Live music every Thursday night with free entry. Or our comedy night on the first Wednesday of every month. Check the website for listings.

VINTAGE MUSIC BAR WITH LARGE COURTYARD

Stylish vintage décor sets the scene in Hirst's Yard and the well stocked bar does the rest. The venue is a mismatched collection of old-looking armchairs, open feature fireplace and aged wooden flooring complemented by a bouncy indie and pop soundtrack.

There is a list of around 10 cocktails, a decent selection of spirits and an extensive choice of beers and lagers from around the world. Hirst's Yard is a stones throw from Call Lane and has a large outdoor courtyard which gets packed in summer months.

MEAN-EYED CAT BAR

BAR | CITY CENTRE

14 Merrion Street
LS1 6PQ

SUN, WED & THU | 17:00 - 02:00
FRI - SAT | 17:00 - 04:00

0113 244 4080
www.meaneyedcatbar.co.uk

WHY NOT TRY?

Home of unlimited free pizza - free pizza with any drink between 5pm-9pm

BOLD, BUT NEVER BRASH, ALWAYS EXPECT A WARM WELCOME!

Mean-Eyed Cat Bar prides itself on being a totally unpretentious and effortlessly cool drinking den. The decor inside feels as if somewhere from the south of the USA has been dropped into the heart of Leeds. An extensive and enticing cocktail menu, craft beer taps pour out brews in conjunction with Northern Monk Brew Co, including orange infused "Orange Blossom Special" and the bar's namesake beer, a 6.2% full-bodied IPA and there is also a "get rhythm" session IPA. An extensive range of bottled products and a seriously well-stocked back bar, that has a focus on bourbon. There are a number of great offers, including their dice cards, where you can roll a dice for a chance of discount. Bespoke handmade pizzas are served up free till 9pm.

MILO

BAR | CITY CENTRE

10 - 12 Call Lane
LS1 6DN

MONDAY - WEDNESDAY | 17:00 - 02:00
THURSDAY - FRIDAY | 17:00 - 03:00
SATURDAY | 13:00 - 04:00

miloleeds@gmail.com

WHY NOT TRY?

The 'lagerita' - a giant glass of tequila, lime and crushed ice with a whole bottle of beer shoved in!

YOUR FRIENDLY NEIGHBOURHOOD DIVE BAR

Milo bar has been at the forefront of Leeds musical history for over 10 years, staff have included members of Kaiser Chiefs and The Cribs played some of their first shows here, but after a few years of quiet reflection its back with a vengeance. A brand new deep-south inspired cocktail menu, loads of blues, Americana and KISS records on the jukebox, a full refurbishment along with friendly staff and cheap drinks (as well as top shelf stuff too...) makes Milo THE spot for people looking for a more rock 'n roll alternative on Call Lane. Did we mention the array of Bourbons, draught lagers and IPA and the great coffee? If you need anymore reason to swing by, most evenings host live music, quizzes, film showings and much more.

NORTH BAR

BAR | CITY CENTRE

24 New Briggate
LS1 6NU

MONDAY - TUESDAY | 11:00 - 01:00
WEDNESDAY - SATURDAY | 11:00 - 02:00
SUNDAY | 12:00 - 24:00

0113 242 4540
www.northbar.com

DID YOU KNOW?

North Bar was the first place in the UK to serve Sierra Nevada, Erdinger, Brooklyn lager and Duchesse du Bourgogne.

PROBABLY THE FIRST CRAFT BEER BAR IN BRITAIN

One of the original pioneers of the Leeds bar scene, North Bar has led the charge for great quality drinks for nearly 20 years, with an unparalleled drinks selection, friendly and knowledgable staff, and a reputation for being the go-to place for beer lovers everywhere.

Winner of the Observer Food Monthly's 'Best Place to Drink in Britain' award, hosting regular art exhibitions and exciting beers to the people of Leeds. In the heart of the city, North is just a few minutes walk from Leeds Arena, Opera North, The Grand Theatre and Victoria Quarter.

In 2015, the North Bar group opened their own brewery just outside the city centre, and proudly serves North Brewing Co beer alongside products from all over the world on its 18 taps.

NORTH BAR HARROGATE

BAR | HARROAGTE

2D Oxford Buildings, Cheltenham Parade
HG1 1DA

MONDAY - THURSDAY | 08:00 - 23:00
FRIDAY | 08:00 - 24:00 **SATURDAY** | 09:00 - 24:00
SUNDAY | 10:00 - 23:00

01423 520 772
www.northbar.com/harrogate

DID YOU KNOW?

The site is right beside the theatre, just like the original North Bar!

BRINGING THE LEEDS LOVE TO HARROGATE

The newest addition to the North Bar family, North Bar in Harrogate ups the Leeds group's dedication to high-quality drinks and excellent service, offering food and coffee during the day and a huge range of drinks including keg, cask, bottled and canned beers as well as a plethora of amazing spirits and wines.

A vast outdoor area is bathed in sun throughout the day, with a function room hosting cinema nights and screenings which is available to hire.

Getting stuck in to Harrogate's thriving independent scene, North Bar brings a bit of Leeds love to our North Yorkshire cousins.

NORTH BAR SOCIAL

BAR | OTLEY

8-10 Bondgate
LS21 3AB

MON - WED | 15:00 - 23:00
THU | 15:00 - 24:00 **FRI** | 12:00 - 24:00
SAT | 11:00 - 24:00 **SUN** | 11:00 - 23:00

01943 468 061
www.northbar.com/northbarsocial

WHY NOT TRY?

North Bar Social's amazing cakes, baked each Sunday by an incredibly talented local cakespert. They don't hang around for long!

BRINGING AMAZING BEERS, WINES AND SPIRITS TO OTLEY

The North Bar group spreads the love a little further out from the Leeds heartland, bringing its dedication to great drinks and service all the way to Otley.

Spanning two floors, North Bar Social boasts the same commitment to providing the very best beers and drinks in the world in a cosy and welcoming atmosphere. Opened in 2013, North Bar Social gets stuck in to the bustling Otley bar and pub community.

Proud host of the North Bar Social Cycling Club, this pocket-sized bar is all about getting stuck into local goings on, with a function room available to hire for free for parties, events and local groups.

THE OFFICE BAR

BAR | CITY CENTRE

9 East Parade
LS1 2AJ

MONDAY - THURSDAY | 17:00 - LATE
FRIDAY - SATURDAY | 14:00 - 02:00
SUNDAY | CLOSED

07988 800 078

f

WHY NOT TRY?

One of our many regional ciders or beers, which vary month to month?

A TRUE INDEPENDENT CONCEPT BAR IN THE HEART OF THE CITY

With its contemporary interior yet rustic feel, The Office Bar is a great little hideaway at the end of the revived Greek Street. It's no dress code policy and relaxed atmosphere are reminiscent of an old fashioned local, creating the feeling of being a home away from home.

Offering a good selection of wines and a wide range of spirits, it's the premium brands at affordable prices that really draw people in. The assortment of craft ales and lagers, as well as unknown beers and ciders, make for an emporium of discovery - it's beer drinking reinvented. Here you are always guaranteed a warm welcome, and the bar is also available midweek for hire.

Don't forget to ask the staff about the 'Cheesecake'!

OUTLAWS YACHT CLUB

BAR & EVENT SPACE | CITY CENTRE

38 New York Street
LS2 7DY

MONDAY - THURSDAY | 10:00 - 23:00
FRIDAY & SATURDAY | 10:00 - 24:00
SUNDAY | 12:00 - 21:00

0113 234 6998
www.outlawsyachtclub.com

WHY NOT TRY?

Outlaws bespoke cocktail range, 2-4-1 cocktails all day every Wednesday!

CREATIVE CAFÉ-BAR HANGOUT FOR MUSIC & ART LOVERS

A unique café-bar/art-space serving own blend espresso, roasted by North Star micro roasters, and our own pale ale, brewed by the Northern Monk Brewery. The majority of the food is sourced from within Yorkshire. Their breads are from The Leeds Bread Co-op, and the cheese board is handpicked from the best Yorkshire cheeses, while the meat platter is from a farm in Holmfirth. A laid back coffee shop by day there's free Wi-Fi with plenty of plug sockets for freelancers & comfy spaces for meetings, plus a large selection of vintage board games, kids books & lego to play with.

By night Outlaws transforms into a cool beer & cocktails lounge and is host to an interesting range of DJs, Artists, Musicians & Authors.

PRESTON

BAR | ROUNDHAY

PRESTON

468 Roundhay Road
LS8 2HU

MON - WED | 15:00 - 23:00
THU - FRI | 15:00 - 23:30
SAT | 13:00 - 23:30 **SUN** | 13:00 - 22:30

0113 249 4709
www.northbar.com/preston

DID YOU KNOW?
Preston is named after the Preston family who built the building in 1898. The name can be found emblazoned in a beautiful mosaic at the door's threshold.

MARVELLOUS DRINKS IN BEAUTIFUL SURROUNDINGS

A hop, skip and a jump from Roundhay Park, Preston is part of North Bar, and continues the group's dedication to fabulous service and high-quality drinks in the local suburb of Oakwood. No trip to the park is complete without a pit-stop at your favourite local.

With its sunny outdoor terrace and cosy interiors, Preston is perfect for lazy summer afternoons and cold wintry evenings too. Like the other bars in the North Bar group, Preston boasts a huge selection of beers, wines, spirits and soft drinks from all over the world.

ROXY BALLROOM

PING PONG BAR | CITY CENTRE

Albian Street / Boar Lane
LS1 6HW

MONDAY - THURSDAY | 15:00 - 01:00
FRIDAY - SATURDAY | 12:00 - 03:00
SUNDAY | 12:00 - 01:00

0113 322 1781
www.roxyballroom.co.uk

WHY NOT TRY?

A fun game of Beer Pong with your friends. Subscribe to their website to receive regular promotions and vouchers.

PING PONG & POOL MEETS PIZZA AND PINTS

This expansive stripped-back space is packed with ping pong and pool tables aimed at bringing out the big kid in you.

Its huge, cleverly-separated interior marks sections for ping pong and beer pong drinking games, a row of pool tables and seated sections.

They serve delicious fresh dough pizza, home made burgers and a range of tapas style nibbles. There are lots of beers and lagers including Asahi, Cobra, Whitstable Pale Ale alongside some local products.

It has an amazing atmosphere powered by a Rock/Indie classic soundtrack and even offers VIP room hire

ROXY LANES

BOWLING ALLEY BAR | CITY CENTRE

40 Upper Basinghall Street
LS1 5BQ

SUNDAY - FRIDAY | 15:00 - LATE
SATURDAY | 10:00 - LATE

0113 322 1781
www.roxylanes.co.uk

WHY NOT TRY?

The £5 Monday event, £5 bowling, £5 for pizza and £5 for two pints of Roxy Lager.

EAT, DRINK & BOWL

Roxy Lanes is tucked away above Tesco, in Upper Basinghall Street and houses a cocktail bar with 4 ultra modern bowling lanes.

Roxy Lanes serves delicious fresh dough pizza, home made burgers and a range of tapas style nibbles.

There are lots of beers and lagers to choose from including Asahi, Cobra, Whitstable Pale Ale alongside some local products.

Roxy Lanes has something very unique. It's hugely popular for groups, which makes it a great hangout spot, be it Saturday daytime or late at night.

THE SHED

BAR | CITY CENTRE

6 Heaton's Court
LS1 4LJ

TUESDAY - THURSDAY | 16:00 - LATE
FRIDAY - SATURDAY | 16:00 - 04:00
SUNDAY - MONDAY | CLOSED

0113 244 1198
www.theshedbar.co.uk

WHY NOT TRY?

£3 drinks and 2-4-1 Cocktails everyday between 4pm and 8pm.

LET THE GOOD TIMES ROCK 'N' ROLL

Nestled beneath a charismatic railway arch off Lower Briggate lies The Shed Bar. With an exposed natural brick and timber interior, The Shed Bar generates an electric gig-like atmosphere provided by its incredible array of modern Rock and Indie songs blended with classic Rock 'N' Roll.

There are over 35 classic and original cocktails, a plethora of craft ales and premium spirits and a particular focus on Scotch Whisky; with over 50 single malts stocked - including a mega rare vintage Macallan from the 1960's!

The Shed Bar is really at its greatest with the lights down and the music pumping, this music orientated venue stands loud and proud and has been an established part of the Leeds nightlife scene since 2008.

SLATE NQ

POOL BAR | CITY CENTRE

St Johns House, Merrion Street
LS2 8JE

MONDAY - THURSDAY | 15:00 - LATE
FRIDAY - SUNDAY | 12:00 - LATE

0113 322 5788
www.slatenq.co.uk

WHY NOT TRY?

HAPPY HOUR EVERYDAY - Enjoy a range of drinks at £3 until 8pm

EAT - DRINK - POOL

A vibrant new bar boasting three large outdoor terrace spaces opened in the up and coming area known as the Northern Quarter (Merrion Street). It offers homemade pizzas, cocktails, gaming and plenty of pool all under one roof. The upstairs bar has its own terrace, which can host up to 100 people with three additional pool tables and bar - perfect for private parties or hosting an exclusive event.

THE SOCIAL

BAR | CITY CENTRE

SOCIAL

21 Merrion Street
LS2 8NG

SUNDAY - WEDNESDAY | 13:00 - 23:00
THURSDAY | 13:00 - 24:00
FRIDAY - SATURDAY | 13:00 - 01:00

0113 242 9442

WHY NOT TRY?

Cask Ale from £2.90 a pint, and hearty Stew from £3.50 a portion!

A HAVEN FOR A RELAXED, GOOD SOCIAL TIME!

The Social is a welcoming new bar and hang-out in the city centre's thriving Northern Quarter. A collaboration between much-loved Leeds venues The Brudenell Social Club and Sela Bar, The Social brings together the quality reputation and admirable ethos of both, in a relaxed and attractive environment.

Serving excellent local ales, craft beers and hearty stews at exceptional prices alongside fine music and good company, The Social celebrates simple pleasures done well to create good times for all. Come hang, chat and get social!

THE TIKI HIDEAWAY

COCKTAIL BAR | CITY CENTRE

38 Call Lane (above Call Lane Social)
LS1 6DT

WEDNESDAY - SATURDAY | 19:00 - 04:00
SUNDAY - TUESDAY | CLOSED

0113 247 0285
www.calllanesocial.co.uk/tiki

WHY NOT TRY?

The Zombie; a healthy glug of a combination of rums, pineapple & apricot. Served in a Tiki head with fire & extra flames.

LEEDS' FIRST AND BEST TIKI BAR

Aloha! Welcome to the Tiki Hideaway, the original and best tiki bar in Leeds! Good times are easy to come by in our 1950's inspired tropical slice of tiki paradise.

It's true escapism with its tiki decor and Zombie cocktails set alight with an extra flame for good measure.

Since opening in 2010 and expanding in 2014, Tiki has become an institution for transporting people to a Polynesian paradise.

Tiki pride themselves on their friendly, fun atmosphere and creativity that goes into every cocktail they lovingly serve.

THE TURK'S HEAD

BAR | CITY CENTRE

THE TURK'S HEAD

Turk's Head Yard
LS1 6HB

MONDAY - THURSDAY | 16:00 - 24:00
FRIDAY | 16:00 - 01:00 **SATURDAY** | 12:00 - 01:00
SUNDAY | 12:00 - 23:00

0113 242 3368
www.turksheadleeds.co.uk

WHY NOT TRY?

The Whittaker's Gin and Hop tonic with a side order of Crispy Pig's Ears and pickled curried Cauliflower.

INDEPENDENT BEERS, ARTISAN SPIRITS AND COCKTAILS OF NOTE

Opened in early 2016, The Turk's Head is already regarded as one the most beautiful bars in Yorkshire, hidden just off the main shopping precinct in Leeds City Centre.

Inspired by the dram and liqueur shops that gave way to the gin palaces of the 18th Century, The Turk's Head reflects on the past but remains firmly rooted in the present. The aim is to present one of the strongest beer lists in the country (12 changing keg lines, 2 casks and a stacked fridge), alongside an evolving artisan spirit list and a refined cocktail menu.

Crispy pig's ears and the House Pickle Plate give a nod to the Victorian heritage of the bar's location, while the full menu of neighbouring sister pub Whitelock's is available all weekend.

VERVE

BAR | CITY CENTRE

16 Merrion Street
LS1 6PQ

SUNDAY - THURSDAY | 17:00 - 02:00
FRIDAY - SATURDAY | 17:00 - 04:00
First Saturday of the month : 17:00 - 06:00

0113 244 2272
www.verveleeds.co.uk

WHY NOT TRY?

The weekly free comedy nights (Tues), weekly free live music nights (Sun/Thurs/Fri) and the fully stocked Tequila bar.

FREE MUSIC/COMEDY AND A TEQUILA BAR DOWNSTAIRS

Friendly, independent bar, serving an extensive choice of bottled and draught beers and incredible cocktails.

Verve's renowned for buzzing parties, cocktails, free live music Sundays/Thursdays/Fridays, free comedy Tuesday, plus a weekend tequila bar.

Let the friendly staff guide you through Verve's cocktail range; classics upstairs and downstairs we have The Mariachi Bar, be transported into a Mexican themed tequila bar. There are a number of twists on Margeritas and if shots are your thing there is an extensive range of tequilas, sangritas and veditas.

WIRE

NIGHT CLUB | CITY CENTRE

2 - 8 Call Lane
LS1 6DN

EVENT NIGHTS | 23:00 - LATE

0113 234 0980
www.wireclub.co.uk

WHY NOT TRY?

Nights such as Acetate / Butter Side Up /Rewind / Dancehall Science and many more...

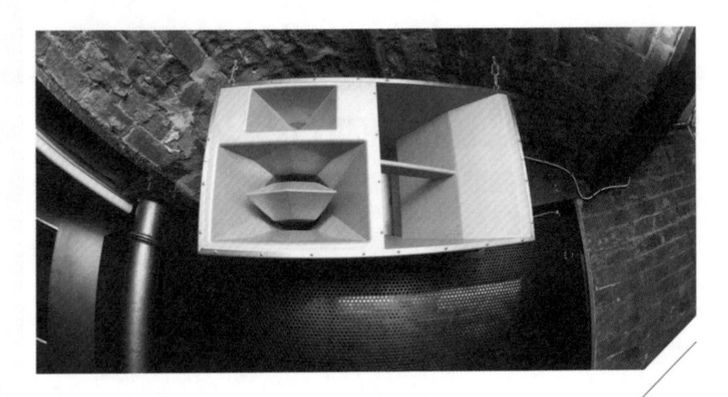

FULL FUNKTION ONE SOUND SYSTEM. INTIMATE BASEMENT CLUB

Wire is one of Leeds' finest clubs pushing quality underground music in a friendly and intimate environment. Powered by a full Funktion One Soundsystem and fuelled by a selection of the best imported bottled beers and spirits.

Wire is host to some of Leeds' longest running and most revered club nights such as Acetate/Butter Side Up/Rewind/Dancehall Science and many more, providing a great selection of events across the musical spectrum.

SHOPPING + LIFESTYLE

INDULGE IN SOME SPECIALIST RETAIL THERAPY...

For those who want to step away from the usual high street names in search of something a little bit different, the independent shops and retailers of Leeds breathes character back into the city.

THE MULTICULTURAL HEART OF LEEDS

by Jessica Wright, photography by Mike Medlock

Tucked into this magnificent building are stalls one after the other, each selling something wonderful. Whether by sight or smell, all stalls draw in their customers with the added charisma of market stall tradition. Kirkgate Market has fascinated me since my first visit to Leeds - glance up and you could just as easily be in a grand ball room as a botanical garden, where the natural light streaming through the rooftop glass (which was inspired by Crystal Palace) is both mystical and fresh – a true gem in the heart of the city.

I've long been enamoured with the charming corridors and main hall, both married with accents and aromas from across the world. Kada Bendaha - owner of the illustrious Cafe Moor - has a mission to make Leeds Market the envy of other cities, and in doing so, has given me the opportunity to explore the length and breadth of the world's cultures, all under one roof.

Kada Bendaha - Cafe Moor

Kada Bendaha, well-recognised owner of Cafe Moor's Middle Eastern and North African bourec parcels and shawarma wraps, has changed the perception of kebab culture in Leeds. He loathes the association of morning regret with his homeland's traditional food, and in that negative, something wonderful - Cafe Moor - was born.

Kada's restaurant-quality ingredients are all sourced within the walls of Kirkgate Market - and he reckons you can make just about any recipe from produce bought here. Kada celebrates local ingredients making foreign recipes, and has huge pride in the quality and knowledge behind the people who bring Leeds Market to life.

Joanne Johnson - The Nut Shop

Over the past 33 years, Joanne Johnson has seen the evolution of traditional traders who have introduced multiculturalism to their stalls, including their own. Nigel greets me with "Dzień dobry! W czym mogę pomóc?" - a friendly "hello, how are you?" in Polish. Himself and Joanne now know greetings from across Europe; Polish, Russian and Greek, bringing a mix of culture to the 60 year old stall.

Many younger customers show Joanne recipes on their phone so she can help - one awesome customer brought them back a huge slab of cake made with their products as a welcomed thank you for helping with her purchases.

许多语言一个声音

Malcolm Michael's

Having made its mark on Butchers Row for 33 years, Malcolm Michael's still-traditional butcher's embraces the multiculturalism that has comfortably enveloped Leeds Market. "Belly pork used to be a throw-away cut," Malcolm grins, "until we learned that the Portuguese love it." It's now the most expensive pork cut.

In the last ten years they've picked up the names of meat cuts in Portuguese, French, Polish, Italian, and Chinese, though one customer tells Malcolm off for speaking too much in her language - she wants to learn better English through conversation! With that anecdote, we wrap up, and he beams "business is thriving".

Steven - S. Myers

We meander down Butchers Row to S. Myers' fishmongers. Steven himself describes the changes he's seen over his 27 years in the market: having mostly sold haddock and cod in formative years, they delved into different cultures by expanding their menu - in both cultural preference and price - a whole Tilapia is only £1, and many customers use the entire fish - heads and all - waste not.

He communicates in his customers' mother-tongue to make them smile - "do zobaczenia" he says, meaning "see you next time" in Polish - it's easy to tell why customers of other cultures feel so at home here.

Liam Tarbett -
Tarbett's Fishmongers

Tarbett's sees a change in customer from weekday to weekend. 80% of his midweek customers are Chinese and West Indian, whereas on weekends, more British people venture to his fishmongers.

Liam's 3 year old stall specialises in whole fish, whereas his Chapel Allerton store primarily sells white fillets - he clearly knows his customer base, as both are flourishing. Live crabs wouldn't sell much in Chapel A, but by 4pm on a Tuesday he'd sold 2.5 boxes in the Market! Liam explains that Chinese customers often prefer female crabs, as their meat is browner. It's tid-bits of knowledge like this that you wouldn't find in supermarkets!

Farida Koheealee - Spice Corner

Mauritian born Farida's 32 years in the market have seen a dramatic cultural shift: once serving mostly white English folk wanting tips on authentic curry recipes, the majority of her custom now is African, Middle Eastern and Asian.

Her stall brims with exotic shapes, textures and hues, although if cooking with smoked chillies isn't your forte, or you want to cook her traditional Mauritian dish, Daude Di Viande, don't be put off by the perhaps unfamiliar food, or for fear of sounding ignorant, as she'll happily answers a ton of inquisitive questions – in English, French, Portuguese and Spanish!

Jayne Ford - Alan Brown Flowers

Alan Brown Flowers is run by Jayne Ford, whose entrance location ensures her market knowledge is regularly tested. Her know-how on floristry serves a bunch of nationalities, as of course, flowers are cherished the world over.

Every culture has preferences and celebratory traditions, which Jayne observes, and in turn benefits from - her impressively self-taught Polish Christening wreaths, which traditionally surround tall candles, are now sought after by many.

Speaking flutters of Farsi ensures a warm welcome to her Iranian customers - who Jayne knows adore a sweet smelling purple Hyacinth for their New Year celebrations, and stocks them especially.

سب زبان یکجا.

Sue and Mick Allen - B&M Fabrics

Much like flowers, fabric is a world-wide commodity. 40 years in the market has seen B&M Fabrics surge in cultural diversity. Their shop window is draped with yellow florals, fragile African lace, and Georgette, which is coveted by the Arabic community.

Sue and Mick have learned fabric names in various languages, vastly improving their customer service to the masses. Sue explains that different nationalities don't register with her, that when something is so well-established, it becomes ordinary. That's what Leeds Kirkgate Market represents so eloquently - harmonious equality between cultures, which as we all know, is a precious thing to take pride in.

Bartesz Prażmowski - TEAPOT (Tea or Coffee)

Bartesz greets me with just-made chai masala tea, and my taste buds do a little dance of joy. Tea is quite obviously the drink of gods, and is medicinal too - although we all knew that, right? Bart's biology background means he knows his stuff, and he can communicate this in English, Polish, Czech and Slovakian.

Teapot, originally from Poland, still purchases from their old local blendery and roastery, as well as honey from a once nearby Polish beekeeper. What's brilliant about Kirkgate Market is that whilst many products are local to ourselves, we can also sample local produce from the homelands of those now settled in Leeds.

Javad Khamseh - Gallery Barbers

Gallery Barbers was a dying stall when Javad took over - after hiring staff in an assortment of nationalities, who speak Spanish, Romanian, Polish, Pashto and Turkish, the once failing barbers grew from strength to strength. Last year Gallery Barbers came second for the best unit in the market, and Javad praises multiculturalism for this success.

Barbers and hairdressers have to be very trusted - when haircuts turn out bad, all hell breaks loose. For someone whose first language isn't English, it can be impossible to communicate what haircut they want (Pheobe cutting Monica's hair in Friends ring a bell?), so when staff naturally speak a person's first language, that place automatically becomes their 'local'.

Dale – Oliver's (extension of Neil's)

Dale's spent half his life working in the market – that's a fair feat – he's still in his 20s! He knows his product inside out. Think you know about fruit and veg? Think again. His loud voice characterises him, and he oozes cheeky confidence – "being a traditional market stall worker is a performance", he laughs. He's a Yorkshireman through and through.

It's not expected that a young lad would know multiple languages, providing impeccably high customer service, but he can communicate in Pakistani, Udu and Punjabi. Spoken language itself isn't a barrier; he understands body language as if it were voiced aloud!

A CRAFTY TOUR AROUND LEEDS

by Rebecca Drury (Reetsweet Events)

Leeds' industrial heritage of making wool may have long since fallen into decline, but people of Leeds still hunger for buying handmade goods, and our city still loves making. The wealth of craft markets, design shops and teaching spots that continue the tradition today are transforming Leeds into a city-wide collective that can be explored anytime of the year - you just need to know where to look!

Shopping & Learning

The Craft Centre at Leeds Art Gallery is a treasure trove of contemporary makers' work that boasts a full yearly programme of seasonal exhibitions, from print to ceramics, with faultless prices and standards of work.

Fabrication isn't just a shop where you can buy handmade, it is a social enterprise that also teaches sewing, knitting and crafting skills, plus works as a space for meetings and collaborative projects, so you can make friends as you make!

Our Handmade Collective provide gifts hand-selected by owners Claire and Natalie, and there's an exciting programme of classes to take part in, from learning to make resin jewellery to folded book art.

Leeds College of Art's evening classes offer print-making, photography, ceramics and much more. Their classes are taught by practicing artists and will fill you with ideas.

The Bowery in Headingley is a lovely little shop and cafe that also has a high quality teaching schedule, including ring making and SLR photography classes, plus a dynamic exhibition space.

Supplies

Fred Aldous is a newcomer to the crafty scene. Spread over 2 floors you'll find everything you need, from pencils to candle wax and much more. The staff are super friendly and will advise on anything you're feeling inspired to make!

Samuel Taylor's Haberdashery is run by a team of nanas whose sewing and knitting knowledge is unbeatable! If they don't stock it, you probably don't need it - they just know.

S.C.R.A.P. is an eco-conscious mill shop on the edge of Farsley full of scraps. You need to join to shop, but once you're a member it's a haven for hoarders and crafters to explore!

For Inspiration

Colours May Vary owners Becky and Andy curate a veritable feast of design books, rare magazines, handmade pieces and one-off delights sourced from across the globe!

Village Book Store recently moved from Leeds Corn Exchange and now sits proudly in Thornton's Arcade. You'll find self-published zines, plus a beautifully curated collection of contemporary art, design and photography books.

Markets

Reetsweet's 'campaigning against crap craft' has been bringing cool handmade markets to Leeds since 2009. There is also a new fair at The Social and this summer sees the arrival of London based markets The Crafty Fox making their debut in the city at The Black Swan.

Kirstall Abbey hosts outdoor markets once a month, featuring tasty food and handmade gifts. Set amongst the ruins of the Abbey, it's the perfect way to spend the afternoon, as long as the Leeds rain holds!

The Leeds Print Fair is usually hosted at Munro House and features maker talks and a high quality exhibition of the best print based artists the city has to offer.

Tetley Art Space occasionally hold pop-up print fairs and handmade book markets, where you can have lunch and drinks in their restaurant in this blossoming part of the city.

Wherever you go in Leeds you'll find that the DIY culture is thriving, and the crafty scene is growing all the time - keep your eyes peeled!

FASHION ARTISAN REVOLUTION

Declan Creffield talks to Sam Hudson from Leeds College of Art on the future of fashion and its place in Leeds.

The fashion industry is in the midst of a shift; the impact of 21st century fast-fashion has led to a relentless cycle of an over-saturated High Street, which has resulted in brutal disposable consumerism.

It's a thought-provoking fact that an item of clothing can cost less than a sandwich. This egalitarian model has its advantages; however, the disadvantages, for instance unethical working practices and conditions, have become well-publicised over recent years, and gone some way to raise awareness and effect change within both the fashion industry supply chain and consumer behaviour.

Our fashion students will be the future drivers for this change. Yes, the industry needs fashion graduates to work in the fast-paced environment of a multi-national, but an ever-increasing awareness of 'slow-fashion' is taking hold, with the grass shoots of a need for fashion artisans to produce beautiful, crafted, niche products.

Sam Hudson, the Programme Leader for BA(Hons) Fashion at Leeds College of Art, explains; "In this age of social media, everything is very superficial and saturated, too much information and choice, but the quality is low."

Sam encourages her students to reflect on and react to this; "It's about slowing things down, understanding the culture and thinking deeper about the wider world of fashion. Sustainability issues, ethical issues, political issues..."

To do this, identifying and responding to skills gaps in emergent sectors of the industry is vital, and Sam firmly believes a designer has to have the abilities to make their own garments. "We do focus very much on the technical skills, pattern cutting, garment production, tailoring." The

resurgence of tailoring and the British menswear boom are two examples of growth where there is already a demand for more expertise.

Making connections through collaboration is also essential in the development of identity and skill; this practice is being cultivated in Leeds through; projects with established independents such as The Hip Store, Lambert's Yard, Neon Cactus and The Belgrave Music Hall & Canteen; offers of sponsorship and competitions, leading to international opportunities for students by the likes of Alfred Brown (Worsted Mills) in Leeds; and projects led by charities, such as The Bone Cancer Research Trust.

From a wider industry perspective, Burberry's commitment to protecting British manufacturing by opening a new facility in Leeds, dedicated to the production of its world-famous heritage trench coat, is a reassuring sign that a resurgence of on-shore manufacturing for high-end fashion is emerging, and in the heart of Leeds.

In June 2014, Lambert's Yard hosted the Centre for Fashion Enterprise's New Market Entry Programme. CFE is the UK's longest established fashion business support incubator, based at London College of Fashion. This marked the launch of the Leeds Fashion Initiative, a

ground-breaking project which aims to support emerging fashion designers with training and business support and re-establish Leeds as the country's leading centre for fashion design, clothing and textile manufacture.

"It's very promising that they see Leeds as a huge city of growth to deliver their first ever New Fashion Pioneer Programme outside of London," enthuses Sam. "It's really exciting that there is this 'hub' developing."

Leeds College of Art also has its own Creative in Residence scheme, which offers an 'incubation' period to develop a fashion brand whilst benefitting from the mentoring and support of the experts and the resources. Those on this scheme are more likely to remain in the city, as Sam concludes; "The good thing about this global village we all live in now, you don't have to be in London. The nature of creative collaboration, self employment, being the way it is, you can be anywhere and Leeds is a very vibrant city."

420 SKATESTORE

SKATE SHOP | HEADINGLEY

420 SKATESTORE

26 Otley Road
LS6 2AD

MONDAY - SUNDAY | 10:00 - 18:00

0113 274 9314
www.420skatestore.co.uk

BLACK CARD PROMOTION

10% Off for all Black Card holders

A ONE-OF-A-KIND ESTABLISHMENT

Located in the heart of Headingley, 420 Skatestore is your one-stop-shop for a wide range of urban and boarding accessories as well as footwear, clothing and spray paint. Run by skaters and extreme sports enthusiasts, the store stocks famous skate brands such as Element, Santa Cruz, Baker, Deathwish, Enjoi, Black Label and Milk, as well as a large selection of top-of-the-range longboards from Sector 9, Dusters and Globe to Z-flex and Penny. As well as skating hardware, the store has a vast range of high-end streetwear, with big brands like Crooks & Castles, King, Reason and Blackscale. The store also stocks top-end electronic cigarettes, herbal vaporisers and an array of water pipes, hand-held pipes and bubblers.

ACCENT CLOTHING

FASHION STORE | CITY CENTRE

11 - 13 Queens Arcade
LS1 6LF

MONDAY - FRIDAY | 09:30 - 17:30
SATURDAY | 09:30 - 18:00
SUNDAY | 11:00 - 17:00

0113 234 6767
www.accentclothing.com

WHY NOT TRY?

Sign-up to the Accent Mailing list to claim 10% off your first order or ask one of our denim specialists to help you find the perfect pair of jeans in store

MEN'S, WOMEN'S AND JUNIOR'S DESIGNER FASHION

Accent Clothing is the longest standing Fashion Independent in Leeds. A warm and welcoming family run business celebrating over 32 years of fashion, focusing on designer clothing for men, women and juniors.

You can find Accent Clothing situated within the historic Queen's Arcade, just off Briggate, and the family have also recently launched their second store in the Bradford Broadway Shopping Centre.

Accent Clothing are well respected denim specialists where they house the largest range of designer jeans in the UK with their infamous floor to ceiling denim wall.

ARC APPLIANCES

APPLIANCES STORE | CHAPEL ALLERTON

92 Harrogate Road
LS7 4LZ

MONDAY - SATURDAY | 09:00 - 17:00
SUNDAY | CLOSED
City Centre shop : Unit 36, Kirkgate Indoor Market

0113 262 6887
www.arcappliances.co.uk

f

WHY NOT TRY?

New graded appliances at a cheaper price, with full manufacturer's warranty

SALES AND REPAIRS OF ELECTRICAL GOODS AND DOMESTIC APPLIANCES

We have been running 'Arc Appliances' as an independent family run business for over 30 years now. We specialise in new graded appliances and pride ourselves with our competitive prices on all major electrical brands. These brands include; Bosch, Nef, Seimens, Electrolux etc. All of our branded appliances come with a full manufacturer's warranty. The domestic goods we provide include fridge freezers, dishwashers, washing machines, tumble driers, electric and gas cookers as well as a variety of different types of integrated appliances. With the purchase of all our appliances with a Leeds postcode we provide free delivery and offer competitive prices on delivery to a forty-five mile radius.

BEER-RITZ

SPECIALIST OFF-LICENCE | HEADINGLEY

14 Weetwood Lane
LS6 5LX

MONDAY - SUNDAY | 12:00 - 21:00

0113 275 3464
www.beerritz.co.uk

WHY NOT TRY?

Our staff are all serious beer geeks and booze nerds - come in and pick their brains about what you should be drinking

LEEDS' ORIGINAL CRAFT BEER MEGASTORE

Beer-Ritz is 18 years old this year – legally old enough to drink the dazzling range of beers, wines and spirits that it sells!

Beer-Ritz is mainly about the beer, from the newest of the new-wave of British and American craft brewing, to more traditional options from the UK, Belgium and further afield. They have been in business longer than a lot of your favourite breweries, and the combined experience of the staff means that they can offer you an informed opinion on everything in store.

Add to that a small but carefully-chosen range of wines and spirits, and it all adds up to one of the best independent off-licences in Leeds.

BLACKBIRD VINTAGE

VINTAGE INTERIORS | MOORTOWN

7 Stainburn Parade
LS17 6NA

MONDAY | 10:00 - 17:00
TUESDAY | CLOSED
WEDNESDAY - SUNDAY | 10:00 - 17:00

0113 269 5231
www.blackbird-vintage.co.uk

WHY NOT TRY?

Blackbird's bespoke furniture upholstery service with expert consultation on choice of fabrics. Or have furniture made at your request.

ECLECTIC DESIGN-LED VINTAGE INTERIORS STORE

Less than a mile north of trendy Chapel Allerton, is Blackbird, a hidden gem of a vintage store. It looks and feels like the vintage emporia of Portabello Rd - exactly what Leeds needs. Brought to you by 3 design fanatics, united in their mutual appreciation of design-led vintage.

Sourced nationwide and further afield, expect to find an ever changing collection of quality mid century, vintage, industrial, design, architectural salvage, antiques, and clothing, including hand picked items produced by local designers. A must have stop on the Leeds vintage trail.

CHIRPY

DESIGN SHOP | CHAPEL ALLERTON

148 Harrogate Road
LS7 4NZ

TUESDAY - SATURDAY | 10:00 - 18:00
SUNDAY - MONDAY | CLOSED

0113 266 0062
www.chirpystore.co.uk

WHY NOT TRY?

One of Chirpy's Creative Parties, a great way to have a hen do or private party with a difference!

DESIGN TO MAKE YOU FEEL FINE!

Chirpy is a lovely, friendly independent lifestyle design store in Chapel Allerton, stocking affordable contemporary gifts and home accessories with personality, character and style, for all ages.

All the goodies in store are sourced from British designers and makers, many from Yorkshire, and many can't be found anywhere else in Leeds.

Chirpy also run a range of fun and informal creative parties in our upstairs room for hen dos, baby showers, corporate events and birthdays.

COLD BATH

BARBER | CHAPEL ALLERTON

43 Harrogate Road
LS7 3PD

MONDAY - TUESDAY & FRIDAY | 09:00 - 18:00
WEDNESDAY - THURSDAY | 09:00 - 19:00
SATURDAY | 08:00 - 16:00 **SUNDAY** | CLOSED

0113 262 1200
www.cold-bath.co.uk

WHY NOT TRY?

A ColdBath Luxury Wet Shave for an ultra close and smooth finish.

SHARP MODERN HAIRCUTS IN AN AUTHENTIC RETRO SETTING

ColdBath have been offering sharp haircuts and male grooming since 2001. In the heart of Chapel Allerton, the retro, curiosity shop design and cool soundtrack offer a nostalgic step into a different era, a laid back establishment where time stops temporarily...

High quality, contemporary haircuts and relaxing hot towel shaves become your only worldly concerns. There's an eclectic selection of books to peruse while you relax on the Chesterfield.

ColdBath offer a hand-picked selection of male grooming products to take home but you probably won't want to leave.

COLOUR COPY

DIGITAL PRINTERS | CITY CENTRE

Colour Copy Leeds
Colour Print Leeds

46 The Calls
LS2 7EY

MONDAY - THURSDAY | 09:00 - 17:30
FRIDAY | 09:00 - 17:00
Out of hours work by prior arrangement

0113 244 2300
www.colourcopyleeds.co.uk

WHY NOT TRY?

Same day prints - Work can be completed same day, when received before 10.00am.

SAME DAY HIGH QUALITY PRINTING IN LEEDS

With over 25 years of experience, Colour Copy are renowned for being at the cutting edge of Digital printing in Leeds, Yorkshire and the UK.

Colour Copy has always been at the forefront of up and coming technologies within the Digital printing industry. Back in 1989 we embraced new solutions and technologies and during the last 25 years we have gone from strength to strength, applying all the knowledge and experience that we have generated.

Both our Digital printing and Colour copying facilities are state of the art. Our service is second to none and we can produce over 100,000 prints per day. From business cards, flyers, pop-up banners and brochures to large exhibition prints, we are your one stop supplier!

COLOURS MAY VARY

BOOK & DESIGN SHOP | CITY CENTRE

Munro House, Duke Street
LS9 8AG

MONDAY - SATURDAY | 10:00 - 18:00
SUNDAY | CLOSED

0113 244 2704
www.colours-may-vary.com

WHY NOT TRY?

We also have a show space and host a variety of workshops and events. Please check our website for details.

A RANGE OF BEAUTIFUL, USEFUL AND INSPIRATIONAL WARES

Colours May Vary is a book shop also stocking a range of beautiful, useful and inspirational wares. You will find a warm welcome and a beautifully curated contemporary collection in store.

As well as books we stock journals, prints, cards, gifts, wrap, textiles and stationery, sourcing our collection both locally and internationally from a mix of established and up and coming designers. Our main focus is Graphic art & design, illustration, typography and photography.

We believe in everything we stock. If we wouldn't buy it ourselves we don't stock it. Our focus is quality and integrity in both design and production. We are passionate about both the method of production and the final product.

CRAFT CENTRE & DESIGN GALLERY

CRAFT & DESIGN | CITY CENTRE

City Art Gallery, The Headrow
LS1 3AB

TUESDAY - SATURDAY | 10:00 - 17:00
Extended opening hours during December.
Please contact the gallery approaching Bank Holidays

0113 247 8241
www.craftcentreleeds.co.uk

WHY NOT TRY?

...a hidden gem to discover, experience, admire or own a piece of British handmade contemporary craft

BRINGING TO LEEDS THE VERY BEST OF BRITISH CONTEMPORARY CRAFT AND DESIGN

The Craft Centre and Design Gallery Leeds is a unique visitor experience celebrating the very best of contemporary handmade British Craft. Our small and passionate team curate seasonal exhibitions aiming to engage inspire and inform visitors; who can also rely on the gallery as an exciting learning resource. Emerging makers are encouraged in their early careers as well as us supporting more established makers in a gallery environment where works can be owned or admired.

You can find us in the heart of Leeds, tucked away under Leeds Art Gallery steps. To keep up to date with gallery news join our mailing list. Proud finalists of The White Rose Awards 2015 Arts & Culture category.

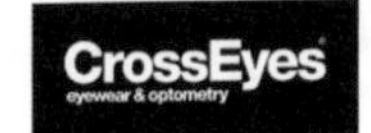

CROSS EYES

OPTICIANS | CITY CENTRE

9 Mill Hill
LS1 5DQ

MONDAY - FRIDAY | 08:30 - 18:00
SATURDAY | 10:00 - 17:00
SUNDAY | CLOSED

0113 245 5378
www.crosseyes.co.uk

WHY NOT TRY?

Our Ambassador Scheme. Customers are rewarded through referrals where every successful referral earns a £20 CrossEyes voucher

A DIFFERENT EXPERIENCE TO BUY EYEWEAR

Eyewear is worn everyday and because people look at your face first, it's also the most obvious accessory out there. We believe that the price should be at a level where you can afford to change your eyewear whenever you feel like it.

The price is transparent and clear on the wall of the shop, always stated with everything included. This means that the fun part of buying eyewear is left, which is finding the frame you like and having your eyes tested thoroughly by our optometrist. Presence and personal service are key elements for us, our concept allows us to spend the time needed with each customer.

There are no hidden cost or fees and our eyewear is high quality, always made to the same high standard. That's CrossEyes.

DINSDALES

ART SUPPLIES | HEADINGLEY

6 - 8 Chapel Place
LS6 3HY

MONDAY - SATURDAY | 09:00 - 17:15

0113 278 1700
www.dinsdales.com

WHY NOT TRY?

One of Dinsdales range of hardback sketchbooks - often at up to half price and with good quality, thick paper

ART SUPPLIES & STATIONERY SINCE 1883

Tucked away on a pretty, central Headingley side street (between Otley Road & North Lane) is Dinsdales Art Supplies & Stationery. A treasure trove of paints, pens, pencils, papers & so, so much more. Now with a room dedicated to card, paper, canvas, mountboard & the like – Dinsdales has been a stalwart of Leeds art & design material supplies for over 130 years now & moved up to Headingley from the city centre 15 years ago. Consistently some of the cheapest prices around. His comprehensive range will suit all budgets & quality requirements catering to the most discerning professional oil or acrylic painter, casual watercolourist or experimenting student.

Also providing straight-forward printing services, copying & more!

DION SMITH

JEWELLERS | CITY CENTRE

Corn Exchange
LS1 7BR

TUESDAY - SATURDAY | 11:00 - 18:00
SUNDAY | 11:00 - 16:00

0113 244 2333
www.dionsmith.co.uk

WHY NOT TRY?

Our Custom made jewellery with rare and precious gemstones. We also offer same day jewellery repairs and engraving.

RARE & PRECIOUS GEMSTONE SPECIALISTS

Dion Smith is an independent jeweller based in The Corn Exchange, Leeds. With over ten years of training and experience within the jewellery trade, in manufacturing, restorations and retail. Therefore we are proud to be able to provide a wide range of quality hands on services including; custom made jewellery, repairs and alterations, jewellery engraving and we are specialists in rare and precious gemstones.

DOCK STREET TATTOO

TATTOO STUDIO | CITY CENTRE

Unit 1, 30-38 Dock Street
LS10 1JF

TUESDAY - SATURDAY | 11:00 - 18:00

07582 453568
www.dockstreettattoos.co.uk

WHY NOT TRY?

Custom tattooing... Get in touch to book an appointment to discuss your artwork!

CUSTOM ELECTRIC TATTOOING

Dock Street Tattoos were established in 2013 and work out of a private studio in Leeds city centre. Custom tattooing brought to you by artists Mitchell Allenden and Rich Wells. With regular guest artists visiting from around the globe.

Get in touch to discuss appointments and availability via email, phone, or pop in for a brew.

ELEDA HATS

MILLINERY BOUTIQUE | GUISELEY

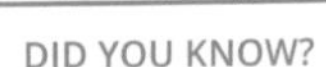

10 Bradford Road
LS20 8NH

THURSDAY - FRIDAY & TUESDAY | 10:00 - 17:30
WEDNESDAY & SATURDAY | 10:00 - 17:00
SUNDAY - MONDAY | CLOSED

01943 876 212
www.eledahats.co.uk

DID YOU KNOW?

All of the hats and fascinators purchased from Eleda Hats can be re-dyed and redressed at a fraction of the original price.

BESPOKE MILLINERY BOUTIQUE

Eleda Hats are a successful, bespoke millinery boutique, established 25 years ago by lead designer Adele Woodrow. Having trained at the London College of Fashion on a milliner's course, where Adele was discovered and selected by the Queens official milliner Phillip Somerville for the prestigious role of his apprentice milliner.

At Eleda hats every customer is unique and we offer a friendly and professional service from start to finish. We can match any outfit from dress to shoes with bespoke and original designs, simply bring your outfit and ideas for a free consultation by Adele and her team.

Eleda Hats have been recognised and featured in many high profile magazines including Royal Ascot, Vogue and Living Magazine.

ENKELHED

INTERIOR STORE | ONLINE

Visit their online store 24/7

07889 256 234
www.enkelhed.co.uk

DID YOU KNOW?

...that Enkelhed means simplicity? Browse our store to find quality products to enhance your home. It's simplicity itself.

CREATIVELY STYLISH, BORNE OUT OF SIMPLICITY

ENKELHED was established in 2015 and created from our passion for interior design and our background in retail. ENKELHED translates from Danish as "Simplicity" and it is our love of high quality, yet simple design that shapes our store and our products and shows that simplicity creates inspiring style.

We are a Leeds based indie store offering well made, hard wearing and long lasting lifestyle and interior goods for you and your home. All housed in a laid back, no fuss store allowing for a friendly shopping experience. We pride ourselves on exceptional customer service and we are delighted to assist with design ideas and inform your choices.

You'll be welcome whenever you visit ENKELHED.

E-STREET BARBER CO.

BARBERS | HYDE PARK

11A Headingley Lane
LS6 1BS

MONDAY - WEDNESDAY & FRIDAY | 09:00 - 18:00
THURSDAY | 09:00 - 19:00
SATURDAY | 09:00 - 17:00

0113 274 8451
www.estreetbarberco.com

WHY NOT TRY?

Student cuts only £10 Monday - Friday before midday!

CUTTING HAIR LIKE "THE BOSS"

E-Street Barber Co. is a gentlemen's barber shop located on the edge of Leeds city centre in Hyde Park – a district renowned for its hip student population and cultural diversity.

The shop was established in 2014 by Mark Jones, a young Leeds native who had trained as a hairdresser before working in two of the city's most celebrated barbers.

Inspired by Mark's passion for music and its cultural significance, E-Street Barber Co. has stylish simplicity at its heart. Adorned with pictures of musical icons past and present, the shop's friendly and laid back atmosphere is the perfect place for a killer cut and a chance to become acquainted with new people, music and interests. Come in and share your stories.

FABRICATION CRAFTS

CRAFT SPACE / SHOP | CITY CENTRE

The Light, The Headrow
LS1 8TL

MON & TUE | 10:30 - 18:00
WED, THU & SAT | 10:30 - 20:00
FRI | 10:30 - 19:00 **SUN** | 10:30 - 16:30

0113 243 9140
www.fabric-ation.co.uk

WHY NOT TRY?

Using our Spice Union spice mixes, make Pork and Pineapple with Coriander Rice and Pinto Beans. Recipe available instore and on our blog

LEEDS INDEPENDENT DEPARTMENT STORE

A social enterprise supporting micro crafts and design businesses. We have everything from food to furniture, clothing, jewellery, accessories, art, photography, toys, homewares, body products, musical instruments, heritage crafts and even a wedding department, made by over 70 local artists and craftspeople.

Many items are one off designer pieces and most of our sellers can also make bespoke to your requirements.

Plus we have a treatment room and meeting room for hire. We also run hen parties and corporate events, as well as craft classes in-house and in the community and ad hoc workspace for crafts people.

FIT TO BUST

LINGERIE BOUTIQUE | CHAPEL ALLERTON

Fit to Bust

6 Stainbeck Corner
LS7 3PG

MONDAY - SATURDAY | 10:00 - 17:00
SUNDAY | CLOSED

0113 3070011
www.fittobust.com

WHY NOT TRY?

To match or not to match: Women talk about matching lingerie, the spirit of play, and why mix-and-match can still be sexy and fashion-forward.

BRA FITTERS ARE THE HIGH PRIESTESSES OF LINGERIE

Owner Sally McGann opened her Lingerie shop in 2000, having previously owned a Health Spa, she saw it as an important step towards women becoming more conscious about breast care. "We believe that what makes us special and different to many other stores is our ability to help ladies feel great in the lingerie they are wearing, whilst also being confident they are investing in the best possible choices for their health and breast care".

FRED ALDOUS

ARTS & CRAFTS SUPPLIES | CITY CENTRE

34 Kirkgate
LS2 7DR

MONDAY - SATURDAY | 09:00 - 17:30
SUNDAY | 11:00 - 17:00

0113 243 3531
www.fredaldous.net

DID YOU KNOW?

We work hard to preserve analogue photography; which is why we stock film, darkroom chemicals & photographic paper.

ART, CRAFT AND GIFT STORE

We are an arts, crafts and gift retailer that has been trading since 1886. Our family run, independent business has now crossed the Pennines from Manchester to help people make anything in Leeds.

You will find everything you need to make anything you want, from fine art materials and model making tools to haberdashery and craft supplies.

We are pleased to now stock a range of our own brand products, which includes the Fred Aldous Block Printing Kit, our Sketchpad range with limited edition covers produced by local artists and our high quality picture frames.

We can provide the right tool or material for whatever project you might be working on, because we love people who want to create.

THE GENTLEMAN'S BARBER

BARBERS | KIRKSTALL

388 Kirkstall Road
LS4 2HQ

MONDAY - FRIDAY | 09:00 - LATE
SATURDAY | 09:00 - 15:00
SUNDAY | CLOSED

0113 345 6112
www.tgb-leeds.co.uk

WHY NOT TRY?

Our hot-oil scented towels will make a man out of you!

SOMETHING SPECIAL IN KIRKSTALL

Kirkstall's best kept secret, The Gentleman's Barber, is something a little different and special for men.

Finally, a barber shop that is tailored around you with no more queuing, a stylish and relaxed feel and friendly staff. Time stands still when you visit us and you'll be spoilt for choice when it comes to which products to take home.

Our services can be adapted for your personal requirements and include; cut & finish, beard trims, hot-towel shaves and The Gentleman's Facial.

THE GREAT YORKSHIRE SHOP

GIFT SHOP | CITY CENTRE

Corn Exchange
LS1 7BR

MONDAY - SATURDAY | 10:00 - 18:00
SUNDAY | 10:30 - 16:30
*Open late night Thursdays during summer and winter.

0113 328 0994
www.thegreatyorkshireshop.co.uk

WHY NOT TRY?

Our food pantry and discover local foods by Yorkshire folk!

FINE GOODS FROM YORKSHIRE

The Great Yorkshire Shop hand pick fine goods exclusively from local independent makers, artists and designers of Yorkshire!

The Great Yorkshire Shop is built on passion and pride of the county and supporting local business, trade and the production of British made items. Specialising in selling a selection of quality, hand picked goods from the independents of Yorkshire including cards, gifts, foods, art, homeware, beauty and men's products. All are unique items not found on the high street!

Visit The Great Yorkshire Shop in the Leeds Corn Exchange, it is one of Britain's finest Victorian buildings and a Grade 1 listed building in the city centre of Leeds.

HIP STORE

MENSWEAR STORE | CITY CENTRE

84 - 86 Vicar Lane
LS1 7JH

MONDAY - SATURDAY | 09:00 - 18:00
SUNDAY | 11:00 - 17:00

0113 246 0347
www.thehipstore.co.uk

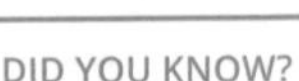

DID YOU KNOW?

There are over 100 different brands on offer including: Barbour, Norse Projects, Ralph Lauren, Adidas Originals.

INDEPENDENT GOODS SUPPLY SINCE 1987

For nearly 30 years The Hip Store has been carefully hand selecting the finest menswear and sought after premium brands. Founded by Everton Campbell and former business partner Umberto in 1987, in the heart of Leeds where the doors of Hip continue to open daily, serving the city's cultured, informed and creative community.

Consistently pushing the boundaries of menswear, The Hip Store curates a stock of brands, often overlooked by others. However Everton's keen eye for detail and construction ensure every garment sold by Hip is expertly crafted and of the highest quality.

The staff will give you that personal touch to your shopping experience and a relaxed atmosphere.

JACKRABBITS POTTERY

POTTERY STUDIO | ROUNDHAY

633A Roundhay Road
LS8 4BA

TUESDAY - FRIDAY | 10:00 - 17:00
SATURDAY | 10:00 - 18:00
SUNDAY | 11:00 - 17:00

0113 318 9315
www.jackrabbitspottery.com

WHY NOT TRY?

Ladies' Night; an evening of pottery, pizza & wine, held monthly.
Don't forget we offer 10% Student Discount, with a valid NUS card!

CREATE HAND-PAINTED CERAMIC LOVELINESS

Now into their 3rd year, Jackrabbits has become a firm favourite for adults and children of all abilities to explore their creative sides. Offering a choice of over 100 pottery items, with reference books, tips and tools to help you create your own personal masterpiece! They provide the relaxed atmosphere and inspiration; just bring your imagination and enthusiasm.

Jackrabbits are very proud to serve a variety of wonderful drinks, from carefully selected suppliers. Coffee from Leeds' own North Star Roastery, a menu of delicious Kandula Tea and not forgetting the legendary 'Wicked' hot chocolate, made with ethically-sourced, artisan chocolate, from Jaz & Juls. Available in 5 delicious flavours! All this, and homemade cakes too!

JUMBO RECORDS

RECORD SHOP | CITY CENTRE

5 -6 St Johns Centre
LS2 8LQ

MONDAY - FRIDAY | 09:30 - 17:30
SATURDAY | 09:00 - 17:30
SUNDAY | 11:00 - 17:00

0113 245 5570
www.jumborecords.co.uk

WHY NOT TRY?

Picking the brains of the Jumbo staff to let them provide you with an instant introduction to any genre of music.

A HUB FOR THE LOCAL MUSIC SCENE

Jumbo Records is a long-established independent record shop in Leeds city centre. They stock vinyl and CDs for genres across the board, from rock, pop, indie, electronica, punk, dance, reggae, soul, blues, jazz and country to folk from all corners of the globe.

They also sell concert tickets for venues across Yorkshire, magazines and accessories. Friendly and inclusive, the shop has long been a hub for the local music scene, stocking home-made CDs and records as well as providing space for bands to advertise their gigs.

KEITH JAMES
MENSWEAR | HORSFORTH

KEITH JAMES
MENSWEAR

124 - 128 Town Street
LS18 4AQ

MONDAY - SATURDAY | 09:00 - 17:30
SUNDAY | CLOSED
*If you would like an appointment, please call the store

0113 258 2605
www.keithjamesmenswear.co.uk

WHY NOT TRY?

Browsing their high end men's shoe collections to match a perfect outfit...

THE BEST MENSWEAR IS OUT OF TOWN

Established for 40 years, Keith James have a reputation for selling some of the finest menswear available in the Leeds area. Trading out of a fine detached Victorian building in Horsforth on the outskirts of Leeds, they have a range of both casual and formal clothing not normally found outside the city centre.

Their brand portfolio for 2015 includes Hugo Boss, Gant, John Smedley, Eton, Paul & Shark and Hackett.

The clothing range is also complimented by footwear from Loake, Barker, Sebago and Hugo Boss.

LEEDS PRINTING COMPANY

PRINTERS | CITY CENTRE

30 - 38 Dock Street
LS10 1JF

MONDAY - FRIDAY | 08:30 - 17:00

0113 322 6442
www.leedsprintingcompany.co.uk

WHY NOT TRY?

500 x 450gsm Velvet Touch Business Cards for £40.

PROPER PRINT & DESIGN RIGHT HERE IN YORKSHIRE

We are a friendly and affordable print and design company based on the beautiful cobbled stones of Dock Street in Leeds City Centre. Leeds Printing Company focuses on high quality print and design at low prices with a friendly, customer-centric approach. We work closely with small independent businesses in Leeds and Yorkshire, as well as larger companies like the NHS and Asda. Our main print offering is around marketing material and stationery, products such as business cards, flyers, brochures, letterheads and compliment slips. Other products include stickers, folders, signage, posters and more. A design service is also available to help set out print ready artwork or to create whole designs and brands from scratch.

THE LEEDS LIBRARY

LIBRARY | CITY CENTRE

18 Commercial Street
LS1 6AL

MON, WED & FRI | 09:00 - 17:00
TUE | 09:00 - 18:00 **THU** | 09:00 - 19:00
SAT | 09:30 - 13:00 **SUN** | CLOSED

0113 245 3071
www.theleedslibrary.org.uk

WHY NOT TRY?

Sit and relax in our Coffee Corner, you can even bring your own sarnies, reading the latest edition of The Rake or New Scientist.

A HAVEN OF PEACE AND QUIET AND 150,000 BOOKS

Members of the Leeds Library, the oldest surviving subscription library in England, enjoy easy access to over 550 years of printed works, alongside 60 magazines and newspapers and nearly 2000 DVD's and audiobooks in the beautiful surroundings of a Georgian library.

Perched above Commercial Street, the peace and quiet of the Library's New Room (opened in 1880) could be another world - far from the hustle and bustle of the city centre. Serendipity is a wonderful thing at the Leeds Library and 150,000 books await to inspire, delight and excite members. If, however, a particular book is not there then members can just request it to be added to our ever-growing collection. Come and join us at the Leeds Library.

LITTLE LEEDS BEER HOUSE

SPECIALIST BEER SHOP | CITY CENTRE

Corn Exchange
LS1 7BR

MON - WED | 10:00 - 18:00
THU | 10:00 - 21:00 **FRI - SAT** | 10:00 - 18:00
SUNDAY | 11:00 - 16:30

0113 245 6602
www.littleleedsbeerhouse.com

WHY NOT TRY?

A flagon of draught beer to take away, great for parties, gifts and nights in.

HOME TO EXCEPTIONAL BEERS, WINES & SPIRITS

Open Since April 2015, Little Leeds Beerhouse has quickly become a staple of the craft beer scene in Leeds. Curating a selection of British beer by working alongside the best independent breweries across the country, these are matched with a refined selection of rarely retailed Belgian and US beers, creating an offering that ranges from traditional old favourites to those pushing the boundaries of what beer can be. As well as hundreds of bottled and canned beers, LLBH provides four rotating fresh draught beers, available to drink in or takeaway in their brilliant flagons. There is sure to be something to delight any and all tastes, all you need to do is ask!

Wines and spirits from all over the world are also in the mix. A dazzling display for the connoisseur!

MALCOLM MICHAELS

BUTCHER | CITY CENTRE

MALCOLM
MICHAELS

3 - 5 Butchers Row, Kirkgate Market
LS2 7HL

MONDAY - SATURDAY | 06:00 - 18:00
SUNDAY | CLOSED

0113 234 7964

WHY NOT TRY?

A home delivery as a useful gift for that special someone...

LEEDS' NUMBER ONE FAMILY BUTCHERS

Malcolm Michaels was established in 1993 by business partners Malcolm & Michael Saynor (uncle and nephew). Malcolm Michaels utilises the whole animal from nose to tail offering cuts which cater to all cuisines.

They have continued to maintain a very successful business at Leeds Kirkgate Market employing 10 highly trained members of staff. Malcolm Michaels supply meat to many bars, restaurants, hotels and cafés, not to mention hundreds of local families.

They pride themselves in delivering the finest meat possible to the family table. Between Malcolm and Michael they have 75 years worth of non stop experience, so look no further than Leeds' No1 family butchers.

MARTIN'S JEWELLERY BOX

JEWELLERS | MORLEY

88A Queen Street
LS27 9EB

TUESDAY - FRIDAY | 09:30 - 17:00
SATURDAY | 09:30 - 16:30
SUNDAY - MONDAY | CLOSED

0113 252 0821

WHY NOT TRY?

The jewellery repair service; Martin personally undertakes the repair and restoration of gold and silver jewellery.

EXPERT JEWELLER PROVIDING EXCEPTIONAL REPAIR SERVICE

Martin's Jewellery Box is a unique gem of a store oozing a rare expertise and craftsmanship that sets the place apart. Enter the inviting décor and charming atmosphere to discover a treasure trove of beautiful, individual jewellery and experience a personal service to fulfil your wishes.

With a vast array of intriguing gold, silver and gem stone jewellery at exceptional prices, Martin's Jewellery Box is the ideal spot to spoil yourself with a special gift or treat your loved ones to that perfect present.

MOD:

HAIR SALON | CHAPEL ALLERTON

mod: SALONS

98 Harrogate Road
LS7 4LZ

MONDAY | 09:00 - 17:00
TUESDAY - FRIDAY | 09:00 - 20:00
SATURDAY | 08:00 - 16:00

0113 262 3185
www.modsalons.co.uk

WHY NOT TRY?

Kerasilk Keratin Treatment at mod:salons. Kerasilk is a great treatment that can be customised unlike other similar treatments. Book a consultation!

AN UNSURPASSED HAIRDRESSING EXPERIENCE

Mod: is co-owned by one of Leeds' most respected men's hairdressers and American Crew International All-Star, Izaak Brading. Started in Leeds in 2008, mod: began life as a men's hairdressing business and after 4 successful years, has grown and evolved to become a fully fledged unisex salon with his business partner, James Langley, British Hairdresser of the Year Finalist 2007 and one of Leeds' best ladies hairdressers. Together, James and Izaak have set out to challenge the way we think about traditional unisex hairdressers.

And with 2016 set to be an exciting year of change with a complete salon refit and re-brand, it is a great time to visit us and experience the exceptional!

MORLAND BATHROOMS

BATHROOM STORE | CITY CENTRE

21 High Court Lane
LS2 7EU

MONDAY - FRIDAY | 09:00 - 17:00
SATURDAY | 09:00 - 15:30
SUNDAY | CLOSED

0113 245 3108
www.morlandbathrooms.com

DID YOU KNOW?

Morlands celebrate their 70th birthday this year. Three generations of family have guided it's evolution from a plumbers' merchant to the luxury showroom of today.

HERE TO SATISFY YOUR BATHROOM ASPIRATIONS

Morlands Leeds have been an independent bathroom specialist in Leeds for over 65 years, we are a family run business spanning three generations.

Our vast experience enables us to offer quality brands, unique designs and unrivalled choice. The best of European and British brands, including Villeroy & Boch, Duravit, Keuco, Keramag, Matki, Hansgrohe and many more bathrooms, showers and bathroom accessories can be viewed in our showroom. We also have a dedicated Hansgrohe and Aqualisa Digital showering area to satisfy your aspirations.

Quality shower enclosures, wet room solutions and made to measure glass screens or bespoke cubicles, are all possibilities from Morlands.

MY VIBRANT HOME

HOMEWARES SHOP | CITY CENTRE

My Vibrant Home

7 Grand Arcade
LS1 6PG

TUESDAY - SATURDAY | 10:30 - 17:30
SUNDAY | 11:00 - 16:00

0113 440 8007
www.myvibranthome.co.uk

WHY NOT TRY?

Chalk Paint™ by Annie Sloan. It rarely requires any preparation like sanding or priming and can be on just about any surface.

CAREFULLY SELECTED HOMEWARES FROM UK DESIGNERS AND PRODUCERS

My Vibrant Home is the only stockist in Leeds of Chalk Paint™, a decorative paint by Annie Sloan. They stock all 33 wonderful colours and the experienced, knowledgeable team are happy to offer help and practical advice. My Vibrant Home also run regular Chalk Paint™ painting workshops.

The team are passionate about offering high quality, modern homewares with select merchandise from UK designers and producers. The products include ceramic and glassware, handmade cushions and lampshades, throws, hand turned painted lamps, clocks, room diffusers, candles, artwork and cards.

NEXT ONE LEATHER

LEATHER FASHION | CITY CENTRE

NEXTONE
Leather

Corn Exchange
LS1 7BR

MONDAY - SATURDAY | 10:00 - 17:30
SUNDAY | 11:00 - 16:30

0113 246 0856
www.nextoneleather.co.uk

WHY NOT TRY?

Browsing their website to shop and preview some of the great leather products NextOne have to offer.

HIGH QUALITY AND AFFORDABLE LEATHER

NextOne Leather has been established for ten years after first opening in September 1999.

They have remained loyal to their customers giving excellent service continuously, over that period they have been designing leather coats and jackets for both men and women.

Although styles have changed over the years, NextOne's commitment to high quality leather still remains contemporary. Based in the heart of Leeds' busy city centre where you can purchase any item and view their special offers. They are proud to say that they meet or exceed client expectations when it comes to quality and service, each and every time.

NICHOLAS DEAKINS

MENSWEAR | CITY CENTRE

15 Boar Lane
LS1 6AE

MONDAY - SATURDAY | 10:00 - 18:00
SUNDAY | 11:30 - 17:00

0113 234 9200
www.nicholasdeakins.com

DID YOU KNOW?

Nicholas Deakins Retail is also home to iconic men's footwear brand Lawler Duffy, the entire collection is also available in-store.

QUALITY FOOTWEAR AND APPAREL

Established in 1991, Nicholas Deakins is firmly established as one of the UK's leading fashion brands. A reputation for innovative and original design has been gained over twenty years at the forefront of British fashion.

The heritage and ethos of the brand is carried into the flagship store located opposite the Trinity Arcade, and is the destination store for Nicholas Deakins aficionados.

A feature wall of grey split mosaic tiles and reclaimed wooden shelving is complemented with bare industrial ceilings and natural slate floor, to present a fantastic showcase.

NINA HUNTER STUDIO

DESIGN STUDIO | CITY CENTRE

16 New Briggate
LS1 6NU

MONDAY - SATURDAY | 10:00 - 16:00

07590 024 921
www.ninahunter.com

WHY NOT TRY?

...a free, no obligation brand consultation with Nina to see how you can improve your brand identity?

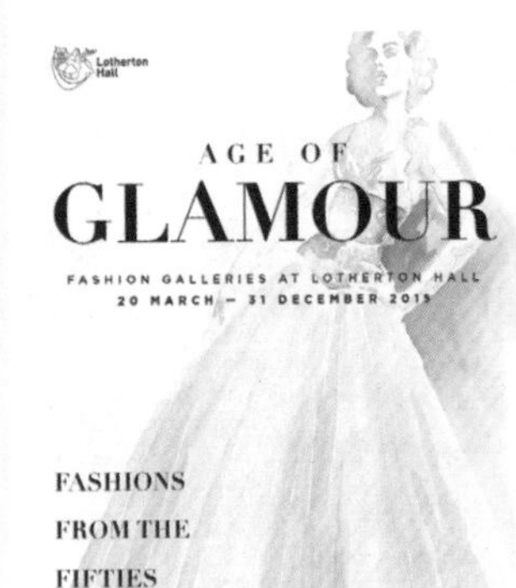

BRAND DESIGNER AND ILLUSTRATOR

Working from her Leeds City Centre studio Nina is an accomplished designer with a proven successful career in branding, graphic design and illustration. Having developed campaigns for global companies including Bose, Asda and Debenhams, Nina decided to put her energy and talent into local businesses. Nina's brand transformations have been recognised as having positive impact on businesses perception and performance.

NORA'S

INTERIORS & GIFTS | ILKLEY

1 - 3 Victorian Arcade
LS29 9DY

MONDAY - SATURDAY | 10:00 - 17:00
SUNDAY | CLOSED

01943 609911
www.noras-shop.co.uk

WHY NOT TRY?

True Grace Home Fragrance, Bold & Noble Screen Prints, Naturally European Toiletries, Stuart Gardiner Textiles. Plus many more!

AWARD WINNING UNIQUE HOME ACCESSORIES & GIFT SHOP

Nora's is an award winning home accessories and gift shop located in The Victorian Arcade in the delightful Spa town of Ilkley, West Yorkshire. Nora's opened in May 2010 and was born from a desire to bring something fresh to a high street that seemed focused on product profit rather than product passion.

Proudly supporting British designers and makers, Nora's believe shopping should be an experience; a way of awakening the senses with delicious smells, bright colours and delightfully tactile objects that cry out to be touched.

NORTHERN GUITARS

GUITAR SHOP & CAFÉ BAR | CITY CENTRE

41 Call Lane
LS1 7BT

CAFÉ BAR : **MON - SUN** | 10:00 - 23:00
GUITAR SHOP : **MON - SAT** | 10:00 - 17:00

0113 234 1976
www.northernguitars.co.uk

WHY NOT TRY?

Test out a vintage Stratocaster with coffee and a cake

MUSICIAN FRIENDLY HANGOUT

Northern Guitars has been trading pre-loved and collector guitars to musicians in Leeds since the 1980s. Many local and international guitar players have been through our doors since then and soon there will be an even better reason to visit... we are adding a café bar to our iconic Call Lane shop. Offering tea, coffee, cakes, locally sourced stews, soups and pies, all washed down with a pint of craft ale. What better way can there be to browse our selection of guitars? Hearty food, proper beer, and guitars sold by human beings who know what they are talking about.

As Leeds' only surviving independent guitar shop, we take great pride in supporting the local music scene. Drop by for a unique café bar experience...with guitars.

ODDFELLOWS TATTOO

TATTOO STUDIO | CITY CENTRE

94 Kirkgate
LS2 7DJ

MONDAY - SATURDAY | 11:00 - LATE
SUNDAY | CLOSED

07907 361 831
www.oddfellowstattoocollective.com

DID YOU KNOW?

Oddfellows is situated on the oldest street in Leeds

TOP QUALITY CUSTOM TATTOOS IN THE HEART OF LEEDS

Oddfellows Tattoo Collective, established in 2012, is an emporium situated in the heart of Leeds. Compiled of some of the leading UK tattoo artists; Tom Flanagan, Neil Dransfield, Adam Cornish, Tom Dooley,Lukasz Andrzejewski and Gibbo.

We pride ourselves on our laid back atmosphere and will gladly chat about your ideas to make sure you get the perfect tattoo, individual to you. We offer a wide variety of styles to cater to all tastes and also have a stream of guest artists from all over the world to ensure the widest diversity and choice.

ON THE WALL

ARTS & FRAMING | CITY CENTRE

12 Boar Lane
LS1 6EN

MONDAY - WEDNESDAY | 10:00 - 17:30
THURSDAY - SATURDAY | 10:00 - 18:00
SUNDAY | 11:00 - 17:00

0113 246 9202
www.onthewall.co.uk

WHY NOT TRY?

On The Wall's bespoke framing service for that extra special gift.

THE PICTURE SPECIALIST

On the Wall is predominantly an art print and poster shop. They also offer a nice selection of T-Shirts which help showcase independent artist's illustrations.

Established over ten years ago in the corn exchange, On The Wall has grown into a picture specialist offering a wide range of services around framing and picture production. The owner and the staff are all very knowledgeable about the products and services they sell and are more than happy to answer any customer queries you may have.

OUR HANDMADE COLLECTIVE

GIFT SHOP | CITY CENTRE

19 Grand Arcade
LS1 6PG

MONDAY - SATURDAY | 10:30 - 18:00
SUNDAY | 10:30 - 16:00

0113 418 2304
www.ourhandmadecollective.co.uk

WHY NOT TRY?

Give the gift of choice with one of our Gift Vouchers... We'll even wrap your gifts for you...

A HANDMADE, HANDPICKED GIFT SHOPPING EXPERIENCE

Our Handmade Collective is an award winning collaboration of 60 local designers working together to bring you an independent, handmade, handpicked gift shopping experience. You can find a gift for any (and all) occasions.

Learn new skills with our weekly Creative Craft Classes – fun, relaxed evenings of crafting, cake, chat and a cuppa! Check our website and social media for the Class schedule.

Described as 'the best handmade Department Store in town', winner of Leeds Love Affair's 'Best Place to Shop in Leeds 2014' and with a number one rating on Tripadvisor for Shopping in Leeds, we promise you that a visit to us is well worth the trip!

OWEN SCOTT

BESPOKE TAILOR | CITY CENTRE

13 Central Arcade
LS1 6DX

TUESDAY - SATURDAY | 10:00 - 17:00
SUNDAY - MONDAY | CLOSED

0113 244 6091
www.owenscott.co.uk

WHY NOT TRY?

A complimentary coffee or brandy while being fitted for your bespoke suit!

BESPOKE TAILORING AT IT'S VERY BEST IN THE CENTRE OF LEEDS

Owen Scott are a bespoke suit tailor of the highest standard using only the finest English cloth.

They are known for their modern approach for tailoring, standing out from the crowd. Also specialising in wedding hire, Owen Scott stock their own ranges which are both modern and individual.

They also offer alterations, off the peg suits and shirts, hand made shoes, shirts, ties and accessories. Why don't you pop along for a complimentary coffee or brandy whilst being measured for your bespoke suit.

PASTILLE

BEAUTY BAR | CITY CENTRE

Waterman's Place, Granary Wharf
LS1 4GL

TUE | 10:00 - 18:00 **WED & FRI** | 10:30 - 19:00
THU | 10:30 - 20:00 **SAT** | 10:00 - 16:30
SUN - MON | CLOSED

0113 246 0700
www.pastille.uk.com

WHY NOT TRY?

Our signature Gel Mani with bespoke hand-painted Nail Art, or a luxurious Spa Pedi in our comfy armchairs.

AWARD-WINNING BEAUTY SALON IN A CENTRAL WATERSIDE LOCATION

Offering nail, lash and brow treatments in a chic waterside setting just minutes from Leeds Rail Station, Pastille has been solidifying its reputation as the go-to salon in the city since launching in August 2013. Clients are devoted followers, both in the salon and on social media where Pastille showcases incredible nail art and fabulous lashes! With over 130 colours to choose from it's no surprise Pastille's Gel Manicure is their most popular treatment, providing the women of Leeds with weeks of high-shine, chip-free nails.

The salon itself is also available for exclusive hire, making it the ideal destination for hen parties or other special occasions! Champagne and manicures – who could ask for more?

PRIME CUTS

HAIR SALON | CHAPEL ALLERTON

PRIME CUTS
FOR MEN / WOMEN

65 Harrogate Road
LS7 3PQ

MON | 10:00 - 17:30 **TUE & WED** | 09:00 - 17:30
THU & FRI | 09:00 - 18:30 **SAT** | 08:00 - 16:30

0113 266 9141
www.chrisjonesprimecuts.com

WHY NOT TRY?

A relaxing wet shave, only takes half an hour!
And for the ladies 50% off your first haircut on a Thursday

LADIES & GENTS CUTTING, STYLING & COLOURING

Trading in the heart of Chapel Allerton for over 6 years, we enjoy a loyal following of local people & their families, as well as longstanding clients from far & wide. Our friendly staff have decades of experience, using the superb range of 'Macadamia' colours, shampoos & treatments, 'Fudge' & 'TiGi' shampoos & styling products as well as a great traditional hot towel razor shave service for the fellas, using the celebrated Italian shave Brand 'Proraso' & the UK's award winning 'Shave Doctor' products. Priding ourselves on setting each day to an eclectic & characterful soundtrack of the best music from movies, funk, soul, rock & downbeat, matched with a relaxed atmosphere & great customer service.

REMEDY HAIRDRESSING

BARBERS | CITY CENTRE

16 New Briggate
LS1 6NU

MONDAY - WEDNESDAY & FRIDAY | 10:00 - 18:00
THURSDAY | 10:00 - 20:00
SATURDAY | 09:00 - 17:00

0113 380 4912
www.remedyhairdressing.com

WHY NOT TRY?

To book an appointment for an outstanding traditional cut throat razor shave by our experienced master barber.

TEN YEARS OF QUALITY

Remedy Hairdressing for Men enters its 10th year of trading this year. Owner Simon Hunter puts the salon's longevity down to commitment, passion and a consistency across the entire brand.

This also includes their gentlemen's hair, beard and body products that have been hand-blended within the Barbershop on New Briggate for a few years now.

While being well established in the city, Remedy still continues to strive for the best in the barbering industry and endeavours to offer the men of Leeds the best haircut, shave, the most beautiful products and first class barbershop experience available.

ROCOCCO SPA

BEAUTY SALON | MENSTON

ROCOCO

103 - 107 Bradford Road
LS29 6BU

TUESDAY - FRIDAY | 09:00 - 20:00
SATURDAY | 09:00 - 17:00
SUNDAY - MONDAY | CLOSED

01943 884 900
www.rococospa.com

WHY NOT TRY?

The Espa Express Facial, a pick me up treat tailored to your skin's needs.

LUXURIOUS BOUTIQUE SALON

Rococo is a luxurious boutique Salon based in Menston, West Yorkshire. Our salon has been designed to create a retreat from the stresses of everyday life. Whether you have only an hour to spare or want a full day of pure deserved indulgence, on your own, or with friends, our team will make you feel welcome and truly pampered.

With product ranges and treatments using the highest quality of products.

In addition to our luxury treatments, we offer a comprehensive range of maintenance treatments including manicures, waxing, eyebrow shaping, electrolysis, and much more.

RUDE STUDIOS

TATTOO & PIERCING | HEADINGLEY

13B North Lane
LS6 3HG

HEADINGLEY : **MON - SAT** | 11:00 - 18:00
LEEDS STUDIO : **MON - SAT** | 10:00 - 18:00
LEEDS STUDIO : **SUN** | 12:00 - 16:00

0113 318 0451
www.rudetattooandpiercing.co.uk

WHY NOT TRY?

20% off for students every Tuesday & Thursday on any tattoo & piercing. Or pick up a Rude loyalty card.

ALL YOUR BODY MODS UNDER ONE ROOF!

Rude studios is an award winning custom tattoo and body modification studio, having two studios, one based in the heart of Headingley and the other bang central in Leeds city centre.

They provide the very best in skilled custom design work and their areas of expertise in body mods covers; tattoos, body piercing, scarification, ear-reconstruction, tongue splitting, implants, laser tattoo removal, semi-permanent make-up and para-medical tattooing.

All with an awesome crew of 9 custom tattoo artists, 4 body mod artists and a strong front of house team.

SEAGULLS REUSE

PAINT SHOP | KIRKSTALL

3 - 4 Aire Place Mills, Kirkstall Road
LS3 1JL

AIRE PLACE MILLS : **MON - SAT** | 10:00 - 16:00
HUDSON ROAD : **TUE - SAT** | 10:00 - 16:00
SUNDAY | CLOSED (Hudson Rd closed Sun & Mon)

0113 246 7510
www.seagullsreuse.org.uk

DID YOU KNOW?

Seagulls save and reuse 127 tonnes of paint from landfill yearly, providing customers the opportunity to brighten up their homes at a fraction of retail price.

CHEAP PAINT THAT DOESN'T COST THE EARTH

Seagulls specialises in the reuse of paint. The paint is processed, blended and redistributed through their two paint stores. The quality is high and they sell a huge range of paint from as little as £2.00 per litre.

As well as stocking new paint and decorating related products, Seagulls also have an arts project specialising in mosaic. Running drop in sessions, one off workshops and large scale community projects they sell mosaic tiles and kits and deliver a volunteer programme that is the core of our business.

SKETCH

HAIR SALON | CITY CENTRE

10 Mill Hill
LS1 5DQ

MONDAY - WEDNESDAY & FRIDAY | 10:00 - 18:15
THURSDAY | 11:00 - 19:00
SATURDAY | 09:10 - 17:00

0113 243 8833
www.sketchhair.com

f

WHY NOT TRY?

Sketch for a relaxing experience in a french boutique salon environment. You don't have to be a star to be treated like a star!!

THE SALON WITH A DIFFERENCE

Here at Sketch we have created a salon with a difference that oozes style, class and individuality. With a French Victorian and Georgian influence, Sketch was born. A collective, vintage boutique was our goal.

Our aim at Sketch is to give you a phenomenal hairdressing experience in a relaxed, glamorous atmosphere. Hairdressing is our passion and at Sketch it is about re-creating - whether it be glamorous or avant-garde.

You don't have to be a star to be treated like one here at Sketch. With a relaxed friendly feel you won't want to leave! We look forward to seeing you soon...

TARBETTS

FISHMONGERS | CHAPEL ALLERTON

128 Harrogate Road
LS7 4NZ

MONDAY - SATURDAY | 06:00 - 17:30
SUNDAY | CLOSED

0113 268 8781

WHY NOT TRY?
Our new touch screen system, with tips on preparation, recipes and nutritional information for each type of fish we stock

THE FISHMONGERS WITH A PERSONAL TOUCH

We are a relatively new business in the Leeds area, having been opened only 2 and a half years. We never stock frozen fish as all of the fish within our stores is freshly delivered every day. Not only is our fish fresh but we also aim to source it locally. The majority of our fish are caught in Yorkshire, from places such as Whitby and Scarborough. We believe in sustainability as line caught fish is not only more environmentally-friendly, being kinder to the seabeds and stock reserves, but it provides us with better quality fish.

We specialise in sushi grade fish such as tuna and salmon as well as live wild crab and lobster. Our fully trained staff can prepare all our fish, from butterflying to skinning and pin-boning.

TRADITIONAL SHAVING CO.

MEN'S GROOMING | CITY CENTRE

THE TRADITIONAL SHAVING COMPANY

20 Grand Arcade
LS1 6PG

MONDAY - SATURDAY | 10:00 - 18:00
SUNDAY | CLOSED

0113 440 6411
www.traditionalshaving.co.uk

WHY NOT TRY?

Using a safety razor for a closer shave and less irritation with blades costing as little as 15p each.

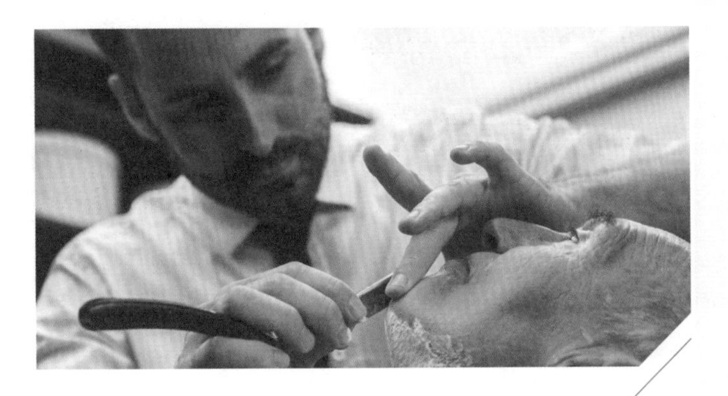

MEN'S SHAVING, FRAGRANCE AND GROOMING PRODUCTS

The Traditional Shaving Company sells a wide range of shaving and grooming products for men.

They specialise in wet shaving products such as badger shaving brushes and safety razors that will give the best shave possible.

Brands stocked include the finest UK barbershops and perfumeries such as Penhaligon's, Geo F Trumpers, Truefitt & Hill and Taylor of Old Bond Street. Barbering services are provided by our resident barber Byron, who has 20 years experience. Services include hair cut and finish, traditional cut throat shaves, beard trimming/shaping and more.

TRAVELLING MAN

COMIC & GAMES SHOP | CITY CENTRE

32 Central Road
LS1 6DE

MONDAY - SATURDAY | 10:00 - 18:00
SUNDAY | 11:00 - 17:00

0113 243 6461
www.travellingman.com

DID YOU KNOW?

Last year we were incredibly chuffed to be nominated and short-listed for the highly-coveted Eisner Award for the Spirit of Retail

THE COMIC AND GAMES SHOP

Travelling Man has been in business for 25 years and in that time we have established ourselves as one of the friendliest, welcoming and well-stocked comic and games shops in the UK. Since we opened our first shop in Leeds, we have grown to four branches across the North of England. We stock a huge and diverse selection of comics, graphic novels, games and merchandise.

We are proud to partner Thought Bubble, one of the biggest comic art festivals in the UK, and we host many in-store signings and events with some of the biggest names in comics. We love to get involved with the local tabletop gaming community, from hosting weekly board game nights to running tournaments for a variety of games, we have something for everyone!

ULITMATE SKIN

TATTOO & PIERCING | CITY CENTRE

33 New Briggate
LS2 8JD

MONDAY - SATURDAY | 10:00 - 18:00
SUNDAY | APPOINTMENT ONLY

0113 244 4940
www.leedstattooexpo.com

DID YOU KNOW?

Ultimate Skin organise Leeds International Tattoo Expo, which runs annually at New Dock Hall, housing over 140 top class tattoo artists.

QUALITY TATTOOS AND PIERCINGS IN A FRIENDLY ENVIRONMENT

Situated in the ever-evolving Northern Quarter of Leeds City Centre, Ultimate Skin is a well established tattoo shop with a fantastic reputation.

Whether it's a tattoo from one of their four in-house artists, a new piercing or a session of laser removal, Ultimate Skin strive for optimum quality. Alongside their in-house artists they accommodate several international guest artists, all of whom inject their own personal style into every tattoo.

Ultimate Skin offer a huge range of styles including traditional, Japanese, realism and more.

VILLAGE

BOOK SHOP & GALLERY | CITY CENTRE

Village

3 Thornton's Arcade
LS1 6LQ

MONDAY - SATURDAY | 10:00 - 18:00
SUNDAY | 11:00 - 17:00
Closed bank holidays

0113 246 9801
www.villagebooks.co

WHY NOT TRY?

A coffee while you browse our books. We brew Workshop Cult of Done espresso using a traditional lever machine.

THE BEST IN CONTEMPORARY PRINTED MATTER. NOW IN A NEW HOME

Village is a book shop and gallery, recently relocated to Thornton's Arcade. We offer a curated selection of art, design, fashion, and photography books and magazines, as well as self-published and small press zines sourced both locally and internationally. We work closely with like-minded artists and publishers the world over who share our passion for the printed form to bring together a collection of unique, limited-edition publications and make them available in a bricks-and-mortar shop.

More than just a shop, Village is a multi-purpose creative space. Our gallery space provides a platform for talented emerging photographers, illustrators and visual artists. We regularly host launches, talks and workshops.

WELCOME

SKATE STORE | CITY CENTRE

22 Thorntons Arcade
LS1 6LQ

MONDAY - SATURDAY | 10:00 - 18:00
SUNDAY | 11:00 - 17:00

0113 234 0185
www.welcomeleeds.com

WHY NOT TRY?

Can't make it to the store? Visit our website, blog, Instagram, Youtube or FB accounts to get a taste of what we are about.

YOUR FRIENDLY LOCAL SKATEBOARD STORE & MUCH MORE

One of the most renowned skateboard stores in the UK (if not the World!), owned and run by skateboarders.

You will always find a huge selection of hardware and accessories in stock, as well as footwear and clothing from: Palace, Polar, Levis, Converse, DC, Emerica, Nike SB, Adidas, Huf, Thrasher, Hélas, Diamond, The National, New Balance, Altamont, Krew, Vans, Lakai, Dime, FA and many many more... Don't Mess With Yorkshire.

WEST YORKSHIRE CAMERAS

ANALOGUE CAMERA SHOP | CITY CENTRE

Corn Exchange
LS1 7BR

MON - WED | 10:00 - 17:00
THU | 10:00 - 19:00 **FRI - SAT** | 10:00 - 17:00
SUN | 11:00 - 16:00

0113 246 0868
www.wycameras.com

WHY NOT TRY?

Shooting on film? Choose combinations of cameras, lenses and film from the thousands of options to suit your photography style perfectly.

FILM & VINTAGE CAMERA SPECIALISTS

Yep, that's right – all they sell is analogue equipment – it's still going strong.

It might seem strange if you're not a photography enthusiast and are used to the convenience of digital cameras, but a large proportion of photographers still use film.

West Yorkshire Camera's new, larger shop and darkroom is situated in Leeds Corn Exchange.

They are open seven days a week, and have a website in case you can't visit – so there's no excuse not to try a proper camera.

YOGA HERO

YOGA CLASSES | CITY CENTRE

The Boulevard, Leeds Dock
LS10 1PZ

MONDAY - FRIDAY | 07:00 - 21:00
SATURDAY | 09:00 - 17:00
SUNDAY | 10:00 - 19:00

07743 513 225
www.yogahero.co.uk

WHY NOT TRY?

Rise & Shine Yoga Flow. (It's better than coffee)

YOGA CLASSES IN LEEDS FOR BEGINNERS TO BOFFINS

At Yoga Hero, we put a focus on feeling fabulous. Yoga is such an incredible antidote to the demands of today: work, social lives, fitness, tasks and errands, family time - there's always so much to do, and not much time to do it in! Yoga Hero is passionate about, firstly, being somewhere where you can have some hugely important 'me time'. We really believe yoga is one of the best things you can do for your body and mind; as such we run classes for beginners to boffins, regular improvers workshops, 'Introduction to Yoga courses', meditation classes and much, much more.

All of our yoga classes are drop in, there's no need to book. We provide all equipment, but we don't mind if you want to bring your own!

therealjunkfoodproject.org

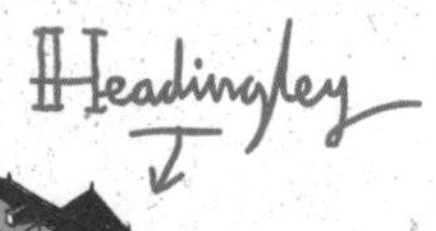

MOORTOWN

Hare Hills

Hyde Park

LEEDS

Armley 1st

THE REAL JUNK FOOD PROJECT

PAY AS YOU FEEL CAFES

Realjunkfood

TheRealJunkFoodProject

itschucho.com

LET'S REALLY FEED THE WORLD

Gabby Papaiacovu talks to Adam Smith, co-founder of The Real Junk Food Project, born in Leeds and spreading good around the world

The Real Junk Food Project is a movement started in Leeds. It began in February 2013, when founder Adam Smith was working on farms in Australia and decided to tackle the astronomical food waste he encountered whilst there. He observed that supermarkets would cancel big orders at the last minute and the farmers would then just plough all the perfectly fine produce back into the ground. It wasn't that there was a lack of food in the world, it was that we were wasting it.

Using his 9 years experience as a chef in the catering industry, Adam and his partner Johanna decided to create The Real Junk Food Project – with the aim to rid the world of waste by allowing equal access to food that would otherwise go to waste, on a Pay As You Feel basis.

Taking advantage of the free public BBQs in Australia, Adam, Johanna and teams of volunteers spent 8 weeks intercepting food destined for waste, cooking it, and serving it to people, whilst educating the public on how and why food is wasted.

A fellow farm worker in Australia, told Adam that if he wanted to change the world he needed to take the idea to his hometown first and watch it spread. So in October 2013 Adam and Johanna returned to Leeds with the aim of expanding The Real Junk Food concept.

On 16th December 2013, the UK's first waste food Pay As You Feel café was opened in Armley in partnership with Healthy Living Network, who offered Adam and Johanna the chance to operate a pop-up café. There began the start of an incredible network of PAYF cafés which were to spread around the UK and even further afield.

After being told that the concept would "fail and shut down all the cafes on the town street"

and that the model "could not be sustainable" the Armley cafe, now known as Armley Junk-tion, generated over £30,000 in its first year of trade. It fed over 10,000 people with 12,000 meals and prevented over 21 tons of food from becoming waste.

The Pay-As-You-Feel-Concept is "allowing everyone access to food, and empowering them to give back their time, energy, skills, or financial donations. Creating an equal and inclusive space for all to share."

TRJFP evolved the concept to a whole new level. At its heart, TRJFP is an environmental and sustainability project - the lowest carbon thing they can do with food that would otherwise go to waste is put it in a belly rather than a bin.

The long term aim is to do themselves out of a job, by demonstrating the scale and senselessness of food waste. "We don't want food waste to continue indefinitely, we're fighting to change our broken food system, to make it fairer and more sustainable."

They believe the Pay As You Feel concept stops the devaluing of food and values the individual.

People have responded in many ways, building them shelves, washing up, sweeping the floor, serving food, cooking food, building a garden and much more. PAYF has broken down social barriers and stigmas to empower and inspire a community of people to come together and feel responsible for a hub of activity within their town.

The food used is intercepted from various sources, including supermarkets, restaurants, bakeries, festivals and markets. So far they've been successful in getting food donations from big businesses such as Ocado, Suma, Morrisons, Nando's, and even our local Leeds Market, however the Real Junk Food team are keen to get even more businesses on board, until food wastage is no longer an everyday occurrence.

After the success of the original café in Armley, Adam received worldwide media attention, which led to people all over the globe contacting them to copy their

model, and so the birth of TRJFP Charitable Foundation network began.

Its overall aim is to protect and preserve the environment for the public benefit by the promotion of waste food reduction and the use of surplus, and advancing the education of the public about all aspects of food waste generation, waste management and waste recycling.

They believe they can achieve these aims through a grassroots

approach to basic education, and in July 2015, Richmond Hill Primary School, Leeds, became the first primary school to open a waste food PAYF café on its premises, with children volunteering.

The recognition of hunger as a barrier to learning led to the creation of Fuel For School, and on 8th December 2015, over 10,000 children were fed breakfast across 4 cities in the UK, using nothing but surplus food. Fuel for School will empower schools to safely feed children, parents and local community members with food otherwise destined for waste.

The key aims of the service are to improve educational outcomes, to enable schools to provide access to food on a Pay As You Feel basis, and to educate children about food waste issues. The project has attracted huge media attention and is already making a positive impact.

The Real Junk Food project now has a network of over 120 cafes, across the UK and Europe and has fed over 70,000 people. However, the cafes are only the start for Adam.

Amongst many more activities, The Real Junk Food Project have begun outside catering and are launching their own beer 'WASTED'.
They're currently spearheading a campaign hoping to see Yorkshire become the first food waste free county by 2018. Ultimately, "Let's REALLY feed the world" is aiming to reduce the amount wasted everywhere to zero

Look out for the full feature on our sister site Leedswelcome.com

COMMUNITY COLLABORATIONS

by Sally-Anne Greenfield (CEO, Leeds Community Foundation)

When people describe Leeds it is often as a destination for shopping and nightlife. Or the largest finance and professional services hub outside London. Or a city that has a growing reputation in being home to some of the country's leading digital and medical technology companies.

This article looks at the City from the viewpoint of the Third Sector. By that we mean the many voluntary and community groups, social enterprises, charities and faith-based groups that, each day, provide help and support in local communities. A recent survey revealed that there are at least 3,500 individual community-focused organisations in Leeds alone. It is this sector that is responsible for much of the everyday community infrastructure in Leeds that supports people through the good and bad times in their life: child birth/parenting classes, child care, support for families, school holiday play schemes, meals on wheels, respite for carers, therapy and counselling, benefits advice, crime prevention, work with offenders, operating community facilities, providing housing, mediating disputes and building good community relations.

The Leeds third sector is powered by approximately 200,000 volunteers, employs over 13,000 staff and contributes significantly to the economy of Leeds.
Some members are very small, volunteer-led groups whilst others are large, with significant contracts from the local Council and the NHS to deliver frontline services in areas such health and social care.

The third sector has a strong and growing focus on collaboration.
By this we mean when 2 or more people or organisations work together to realise shared goals.
In this instance, the shared goal is to help make Leeds a more equal City, providing opportunities for all.

The examples below help describe collaboration in action in Leeds.

New Wortley is a ward based just off the Armley Gyratory. It is one of the most deprived areas of Leeds and sits in the 10% most deprived communities in the entire country. Unemployment is high, health issues are significant and it has one of the highest suicide rates in Leeds. A new initiative, called Our Place, is really beginning to turn things round and demonstrate what benefits place-based collaboration can bring. Every month local people come together to talk about New Wortley. They meet at the New Wortley Community Centre which is currently being physically transformed by having a new building built alongside the current one. Members of the partnership include local residents and business-owners, representatives from the Council and the NHS, medical staff from the local GP surgery and medical centre, the police and other uniformed services. They discuss what the issues are but, more importantly, how the whole community can work together to make a difference to the lives of local residents. And then those residents are encouraged to get involved in making transformation happen from the bottom up by making a difference with local people, not to them. And the early results are very encouraging!

Another form of collaboration is when organisations co-locate in order to expand the services they offer, and benefit from a much closer working relationship. One current example of this is the Gipton Fire Station project. In 2013 some local third sector groups came together because they had identified an opportunity to buy the fire station in Gipton. They approached the Leeds Community Foundation and, for the last two years, we have worked with them to turn this vision into a reality. With planning permission recently granted, we are now working towards renovating the building and turning it into a vibrant Community and Enterprise

Centre. The anchor tenants will include Gipsil, ZEST and Space 2 with several more prospective tenants coming on board almost weekly. Each will offer a different range of services which will bring the fire station to life and ensure it is a space for everyone to enjoy. People will come to the Centre to sing, dance, perform, eat, learn new skills, find a job, attend a cookery course, receive advice and much, much more. The combined results will be so much more than the individual groups could provide themselves.

As well as frontline organisations delivering services directly to individuals, there are also 10 "infra-structure" or "support and development" organisations who provide support to the frontline organisations themselves. Four of them have been in discussions for some time about how they could work together more closely to provide better services for their members. This includes Tenfold (working with people with physical disabilities); Leeds Older People's Forum (older people), Volition (people with mental health support needs) and the PSI Network (physical and sensory impairment). As of 1st April, they now work under a single health and social care contract and are now called Forum Central. Their mission is "to be a collective voice for the health and social care third sector." They are all based under the same roof and share the same phone number and are looking at other ways in which they can collaborate in the coming months.

Another aspect of collaboration is the links that are being forged between private business and the third sector, not in terms of CSR or community investment, but in terms of business transactions. Leeds is seeing a rise in the number of social enterprises that are set up – the term used to describe an organisation with charitable objectives that trades and sells goods/services to provide income to enable them to fulfil their social aims. The important focus on environmental awareness and recycling can be seen in the work of Re:Work, who supply ethically sourced used and new office furniture, and dispose of furniture you've finished with in a responsible and environmentally-friendly way. In Morley, Enabled Works has risen from the former government-backed Remploy programme and they employ a number of people with disabilities at their 12,600 foot factory. From here they provide contract packing, assembly and fulfilment services.

BIG HEARTED CITY

by Andy Fowler (Emmaus)

Imagine for a moment suddenly finding yourself without any family or friends, with no-one to turn to, and nowhere to stay. Where would you go? What would you do? How would you feel? This is a reality for people experiencing homelessness all over the world.

The traditional view of homelessness is of someone out on the street, living rough, visiting night shelters and soup runs. This is indeed a visible sign of homelessness but there are many other people without a place to call home, a place of safety and a place of permanence.

In these difficult financial times much more homelessness is hidden – young people 'sofa surfing'; people squatting in derelict housing; families living in a friends' spare rooms.

Due to people who find themselves experiencing 'hidden homelessness', statistics as to the actual number of homeless people in Leeds are hard to pin down. What is clear is that Leeds and many other cities across the UK have increasing numbers of people without a place to call home.

The good news is that Leeds has many organisations, groups and individuals working hard to support the most vulnerable people in our city. At the forefront are charities such as Emmaus Leeds, Leeds Housing Concern, Simon On The Streets and St George's Crypt. But every individual has a role to play in breaking the stigma associated with homelessness and helping those people at rock bottom.

There are many misconceptions about why people find themselves

homeless. Homelessness can affect anyone from any walk of life and each person has a different story to tell and a different set of circumstances that has contributed to them becoming homeless.

By working together, individuals and organisations can give people the support they need and the opportunity to rebuild their lives. Once this opportunity is grasped, individuals can feel empowered to develop their own resilience and confidence to break the negative cycle of homelessness.

Jacek's Story:

A mixture of things led me to being out of work and having nowhere to stay. I broke up with my girlfriend and lost my job at the same time. This led to me drinking more and things got worse. I couldn't pay my rent so my landlord evicted me.

I went to seek help for housing but no one was willing to help. I ended up sleeping rough because the only homeless shelter available to me was full. I kept checking back, having meals there and eventually they let me stay overnight.

I then joined Emmaus Leeds and have not looked back since. Everything was provided; accommodation, healthy meals and support.

I gained the food hygiene certificate, completed manual handling training, did courses at Jamie's Ministry of Food and Love Food Hate Waste, got my PAT testing certificate and completed a fork lift truck licence.

Being part of Emmaus made me feel part of a family again and has given me the stability to move forward with my life. I found a new girlfriend, am working full time, have my own place to live and my health has improved massively. I don't want to think where I'd be without it. It has given me opportunity.

Look out for the full feature on our sister site Leedswelcome.com

COMMUNITY GOOD SPORTS

Conor Crozier, from Leeds Welcome, talks to Leeds Rhinos, Yorkskshire County Cricket Club and Leeds United.

There is a beautiful connection between the people of Leeds and the clubs they support. Through thick and thin, success and defeat, fans of Leeds' sporting institutions have remained notoriously loyal throughout. The famous Loiner dedication is not only repaid with blood, sweat and tears on the pitch, but clubs across the city are also active within the community, giving back to the city that has stuck with them through it all.

Leeds Rhinos, Leeds United and Yorkshire County Cricket Club each have foundations to make a positive difference and lasting impact on the community. The Leeds Rhinos Foundation, Yorkshire Cricket Foundation and Leeds United Foundation all work alongside schools and community clubs to deliver programmes with the aim of improving health and education.

Leeds Rhinos Foundation's Rugby League Development plan and Partner Schools programmes are driven by a desire to get kids active. The capabilities that the youngsters learn on the pitch, such as discipline, respect, resilience and determination, are priceless skills that can be transferred to education and employment.

"At Leeds Rhinos we recognise just how dependent we are on our community and we are equally committed to repaying this support by helping to change lives through our sport." *Gary Hetherington,* Chief Executive, Leeds Rhinos.

Similarly, Leeds United Foundation's 'Play' initiative and Yorkshire Cricket Foundation's 'Participation' use the power of sport to encourage activity. Through Skills Centre, 4 Sport and Leeds United Girls Centre of Excellence they focus on technical, physical, social and psychological development to help individuals achieve their full potential.

Each foundation also offers a range of education programmes. YCF's core 'Education' theme delivers a wide range of community outreach and initiatives, and LUF's 'Learn' covers topics including rail safety,

vulnerability and post-education guidance. LUF also helps put young offenders on the right path and give those incarcerated guidance upon release.

LRF has set up a purpose-built classroom at Headingley Stadium called TryZone. Initiatives such as Inspiring Champions focus on pride and responsibility to help teach kids essential life skills. For older generations Off The Bench and Work Club assists personal development of communication and presentation skills for job interviews and work seeking.

With such pride in the community comes a dedication to make the City a better and healthier place to live. To achieve this, YCF engage with people of all ages and from all communities across Yorkshire through their 'Health & Wellbeing' and 'Inclusion' objectives. LRF's weight management programme Try Club is an inspiring example of the social inclusion these schemes provide, as the group continues to meet regularly, long after the course has finished.

LRF have also teamed up with Leeds City Council to set up the In Touch Club, a dementia group with the goal of provoking patients' memories by taking part in activities within the stadium. LUF's 'Live' similarly supports those with physical and mental disabilities, children, young people, adults, the elderly as well as those people at risk of obesity and diabetes.

A touching reminder of the life-changing power sport has, and how important a club's role in society is.

"The aim of The Leeds United Foundation is to engage with the community in developing positive outcomes, raising the aspirations of all participants and encouraging healthy lifestyles. We do this by providing opportunities for increased participation and empowering those involved to make appropriate choices across a range of key areas." *Mick Ferguson,* CEO, Leeds United Foundation.

"The Yorkshire community is fundamental to the success of Yorkshire Cricket. We regard our community work as very important and it's vital to us that we support all communities in Yorkshire. The Yorkshire Cricket Foundation does some fantastic work and as a club we are committed to supporting them in order that they grow and thrive." *Mark Arthur,* Chief Executive, Yorkshire CCC.

EVERYDAY INDEPENDENT LEEDS

Our instagram friend Paul Mac shares some black and white images of real independent Leeds.

City Scenarios.

I know Leeds. I know Leeds is changing. Which makes me want to know more. Based on historic traditions of opportunity and energy, Leeds is becoming a hub of Independent activity made up of people who care, who bring vitality and action to the city. My project poses the question 'How does it feel?' showing a relationship between the city and its users and these particular images focus on individuality, uniqueness and entrepreneurial endeavour.

Paul Mac
Instagram @gone_solid_gone

LEEDS IS BECOMING A HUB OF INDEPENDENT ACTIVITY MADE UP OF PEOPLE WHO CARE

THE MISSION FOR LEEDS

Cllr Judith Blake, Leader of Leeds City Council and Executive Board Member for Economy & Culture, Leeds City Council

The mission for Leeds is simple – win the bid to become European Capital of Culture 2023.

Over the next two years the Leeds bid for European Capital of Culture will show the world what made this city great, charting its stories of industry, creation, innovation, ambition and experimentation. The city will create its bid for the title celebrating its relationship with Europe and exploring the diverse cultural offer that exists in all corners of Leeds.

Whilst there is much to be celebrated in the city centre - the explosion of home-grown food and drink venues, the city's one-of-a-kind arena, West Yorkshire Playhouse, Leeds Grand Theatre, City Varieties, Victoria Gate, Trinity Leeds, Corn Exchange, Light Night, Leeds International Film Festival, Thoughtbubble and more – the city's cultural experiences are also lived through its many communities and the people who bring them to life.

Where else would you find a Victorian Baths showing film screenings of Jaws? An Irish Centre that doubles as one of the best loved gig venues in the country? More than 50 community galas celebrating Leeds life in all its

Photo; ©Justin Slee 2016 All Rights Reserved

forms? A training ground for athletes including the Brownlees, Nicola Adams and Lizzie Armistead? Or a series of mills steeped in the industry of textiles playing host to gigs, exhibitions, studios and shows?

It is these unique but often hidden experiences that make up a culture that offers a diversity in art form and scale, not only distinctive to Leeds, but distinctive to Europe too.

Leeds may not feel like a European city at first glance, however hidden beneath the surface lies a deep rooted connection to the continent. A quick look at the game sheets of Leeds United will

reveal a very European squad. Our galleries host the great paintings, sculptures and installations of Europe's most sought after artists. The food of an entire continent is prepared and shared in this one city. The client lists of our digital agencies read like a hall of fame for European brands. Look up at the city's architecture drawing inspiration from Florentine Bell Towers and Gothic arcades that would be just at home above the streets of Barcelona. Cast your eye over the list of DJs and Bands gracing venues throughout the city in any given month and we give Ibiza some serious competition – weather permitting!

Leeds has long been an international city, welcoming cultures and communities across the globe, from India, Jamaica, Italy, Spain, Poland, Germany, Australia and more. Each year the city attracts more and more students to one of its three universities, or its specialist colleges including Leeds College of Art, Leeds College of Music and Northern School of Contemporary Dance. It is said that Leeds produces more artists than any other city outside of London.

We believe in balancing a strong economy, to which the vibrant cultural offer of the city contributes in large part, with a compassion for the people who live and work here. We believe that everyone in this city should have the opportunity to not only experience the many cultures it supports, but to also play an active role in creating those cultures.

It is time for the city to celebrate this blend of European influence and indigenous talents that could only be Leeds.

Follow the journey at
www.leeds-2023.co.uk

THE ONLY LOCAL WELCOME

John Barran, our Editor, gives you a tour of all the exciting parts of Leeds, brought to you by Leeds Welcome's first local city welcome...

Explore and find the best of Leeds with our first local Leeds Welcome tools: Leedswelcome.com and Welcome City Discovery App.

As Independent Leeds allows you to delve deeper into the city's fantastic independent scene, our sister site Leedswelcome.com and our innovative app Welcome City Discover help people explore and find the best that the whole city has to offer.

Leeds has so much happening at all times that we wanted to provide simple tools to ensure everyone, from locals to first time visitors, can go to one place and find what Leeds has got going on. Leeds Welcome tells all, and our Welcome app will direct you to your destination of choice!

Whether you're in Leeds for a day or a lifetime, the amount and variety of city offerings will keep you as busy or relaxed as you wish to be. With activities catering for all ages and interests, there is always something to do, somewhere to go or someone to see. For foodies, shopaholics, culture-vultures and fun-lovers, here's why Leeds will make you happy...

Whether it's film and sport, theatre and dance, or art and history, Leeds Welcome lists an amazing mix of entertainment for all tastes to enjoy in Leeds. Many impressive museums, galleries and heritage sites display expert exhibits; iconic theatres host the best stage talents; popular multiplex cinemas are joined by innovative alternatives; independent collectives offer creative pop-up events; and the city is home to Leeds United, Leeds Rhinos and Yorkshire County Cricket Club. All this together allows Leeds to daily showcase a range of historical curios, established performers and upcoming artists.

Leeds has had a growing impact and increasing influence on a number of music scenes and now boasts many excellent events for each genre. Shows can be found on Leeds Welcome throughout the city every night, when you can discover niche gigs at the likes of Headrow House, or see giant stars at First Direct Arena. The city continues to put on hedonistic dance all-nighters every weekend, and Live at Leeds shows off the latest best bands in dozens of the city's fantastic venues, which the Welcome app's interactive live map will take you to.

Over recent years, a tasty selection of cafés, bars, pubs and restaurants have transformed

Leeds into a food and drink hotspot, proudly celebrating international cuisine and Yorkshire produce to suit all palettes and wallets. The city's reputation for a good night out is matched by the quality of venues and variety of possibilities, from real ale and roaring fires to champagne and chandeliers. Amidst the dizzying choices, Leeds Welcome will help your head know where to start and remember where to end, whilst the Welcome app guides you across Leeds' culinary world.

After 2013's successful arrival of Trinity, the new Victoria Gate, fronted by John Lewis, increases Leeds' claim as the shopping capital of the north. The welcome app can also take you to other areas of the city which continue to thrive, with main shopping strip Briggate buzzing with visitors and locals, city Arcades filled with charming shops and cafes, and the many fine independent stores listed in this very book. Leeds retail is moving the city towards to a stylish future.

With so much happening in and around the city, Leedswelcome.com is the go-to site to find what to do, where to go and who not to miss. Then allow Welcome City Discovery App to direct you on the go to your new favourite Leeds places. Together we hope they provide all that is needed to help visitors and locals alike get the most out of Leeds.

To access this world of information for this city of Leeds, head to Leedswelcome.com, download Welcome City Discovery App for free, and follow @leedswelcome on twitter and instagram.

Illustrations:
Banner @thommilson
App @leegoater.

LONG LIVE THE PRINTED WORD

by John Barran
(Independent Leeds magazine editor)

Here at Independent Leeds, we are ever the contrary bugger. If the world is dominated by superpowers, let's support the independent. If technology is taking over, let's celebrate the traditional. If mass-production is increasing, let's bespoke quality. If the loudest voice is shouting, let's speak quietly together. And if the printed word is dying, let's make thousands of magazines and give them away for free.

So, with that in mind, the independent voice is spoken up, written down, printed out and taken in every couple of months to create the Independent Leeds magazine, distributed through the city's independent bars, cafes, shops and more to your hands, eyes and minds.

We are fortunate to have an amazing community of writers, photographers and illustrators displaying their talents, informing, entertaining, and reminding us what a unique and alive city Leeds can be, and its people always are. You too can join in by sharing your words, your images and your skills, or simply, by picking up a copy and enjoying the evolving stories and the diverse characters that make up Independent Leeds.

IF THE LOUDEST VOICE IS SHOUTING, LET'S SPEAK QUIETLY TOGETHER

"I've had countless compliments on the lettering illustration I produced for the Independent Leeds magazine cover. I think it's down to the creative freedom I was given on the project."
Nathan Evans, Illustrator & Muralist

www.independentleeds.co.uk/publications